PRACTICAL LIFE APPLICATION
FROM A BIBLICAL PERSPECTIVE
KJV

PRACTICAL PROVERBS™

BIBLE STUDY AND LIFE MANAGEMENT
COURSE FOR THE OLDER STUDENT
80 LESSONS

By Dara Halydier

www.practicalproverbs.com

Practical Proverbs

Scripture taken from the Authorized King James Version, The World Publishing Company: Cleveland and New York.

ISBN # 978-0-9851239-0-1

Published by:
TD Publishing
PO Box 3102
Early, TX 76803

Printed in the United States of America

Practical Proverbs

Practical Proverbs is a high school level course that will fulfill the requirements for a ½ credit (one semester) of either Bible or Life Management. Or ½ credit each for Life Management and Bible can be earned by assigning some of the suggested readings found in appendix D. If you wish to issue your student a grade, base it upon the work being done and the involvement with the discussion questions.

This study is also suitable for youth groups or small groups. Assign 5 lessons per week and use the discussion questions for group discussion.

Unless otherwise mentioned, the Bible verses are taken from the New American Standard Bible.

The student will need green, yellow, and blue highlighters throughout this course.

Discussion questions are included in the front of the book. An adult is encouraged to go over these questions each day with the student for further instilling of the lessons and for personal application.

The memorization practices included are highly encouraged to be taught and accomplished.

God's Word is eternal and thus, foundational for every young person. May God bless the study of His Word and bring you long life and wisdom and joy.

About the author:

Dara Halydier is a daughter of the King. She is a mother of five boys who are continuing their journeys in faith and ministry across the United States. She is also a grandma to seven amazing children. Dara homeschooled for 21 years. Dara is married to a wonderful, supportive husband, Tracy. They currently reside in Central Texas. Dara is a speaker for retreats and conferences across the country.

You can view Dara's website at www.abidingtruthministry.com or contact her at Dara@abidingtruthministry.com.

Practical Proverbs

Table of Contents

Practical Proverbs 

Pp

Discussion Questions

Mom and Dad or group leader, these discussion questions will enhance what is being taught in each lesson. Please take the time to go over them with your student(s). These questions and discussions will greatly help your student(s) process what they have read and help them make application to their own life. There are no right or wrong answers most of the time. As you discuss these questions, give your student(s) an opportunity to express themselves and then you give helpful feedback. Be willing to answer the questions honestly yourself and receive feedback from your student(s). Your viewpoints on a lot of these issues will really help your student(s) to form their own viewpoints.

Part 1

Lesson 1 Definitely Different Definitions

1. What is the difference between wisdom and knowledge?
2. How does discernment relate to wisdom?
3. Are you making wise decisions in school? In friendships? In family relationships?
4. How is our working definition of wisdom different than the world's view of wisdom?
5. What knowledge is Godly wisdom based on?
6. Are you spending time studying the Bible to gain knowledge of God?

Lesson 2 Determining Definitions

1. What type of discernment are you good at applying?
2. Are you prudent in areas of modesty? Speech? Studying?
3. We tell our kids, "Just because it is in your mind, doesn't mean it needs to come out of your mouth." Is this a problem for you?

Lesson 3 Detailing Definitions

1. Explain how the fear of the Lord is the beginning of wisdom. Relate it to your own life.
2. Are you daily seeking to gain wisdom?
3. Who in your life is an example of a wise person?
4. Tell your parent or teacher the working definition of wisdom by memory.

Lesson 4 Daring David

1. Jesus died for our sins. Did that include adultery and murder? Is He able to forgive all sins?
2. What was David's reaction to his sin? How do you react when you are confronted with your sin?
3. What consequences are you bearing because of sin?
4. Are you quick to repent when you have sinned?

Lesson 5 Sagacious Solomon

1. Why do you obey God?
2. When you sin do you quickly ask God to forgive you?
3. Is there any sin too big for God to forgive?
4. Are you living life in your own power or letting God lead you?

Lesson 6 Spectacular Salvation

1. Have you accepted Jesus Christ as your Lord and Savior? Tell about that experience.
2. How has knowing Jesus changed your heart?
3. Who can you pray for and share the gospel of Jesus with using the Roman Road?
4. This is your test on the definition of wisdom. Recite it out loud: "Wisdom is…"

Lesson 7 Respected Rules

1. Discuss any rules that your parents gave you that you did not understand at the time.
2. Is there a rule in the Old Testament that you have wondered why God gave it?
3. Look at the list of what God's Word accomplishes and explain how one of these is being accomplished in your life.

Lesson 8 Awesome Audience

1. If you were a father or mother writing to your son or daughter, what advice would you give him/her?
2. What good advice have you received from your parents? Be specific.

Lesson 9 Foolish Folly

1. Explain this comment: Sins committed do not make us a sinner, but rather our sin nature makes us sin.
2. If that statement is true then why must we be born again and not just forgiven?
3. Think of someone you know or someone famous that has the characteristics of a fool.
4. Recite Proverbs 1:5 out loud.

Lesson 10 Faulty Foolishness

1. The Bible states that God is a jealous God. How does this relate to the nation of Israel being an adulteress?
2. Share your paragraph with your parent and ask them to share a time when they acted the fool.
3. Praise God in prayer that even though we sometimes act the fool, we are forgiven.

Lesson 11 Wonderful Wisdom

1. Think about the verse Isaiah 30:15. This is actually a good definition of trust. Do you tend to rest and trust in a difficult situation or do you tend to worry and fret?
2. Which characteristics of wisdom do you see in yourself?
3. Do you desire the results of wisdom that you learned about today?

Lesson 12 Try Trusting

1. Jesus' last words were, "It is finished." What things, other than Jesus' death and resurrection, do you try to make part of your salvation?
2. Do you seek God's blessings or a relationship with God?
3. What blessings have you experienced because of your relationship with God?

Lesson 13 Daring Discipline

1. Remember a time that you were punished and are now glad that you received that punishment.
2. Remember a time that you were punished when you thought the punishment was unjustified or too harsh.
3. Did you change your heart or actions in either one of the instances of #1 or #2?
4. Sometimes God is not punishing us but rather pruning us through the tough circumstances of life. How is pruning different than punishment?

Lesson 14 Seeking a Savior

1. In what ways have you decided to go God's direction rather than the world's?
2. How has God given you the strength to go against the flow?

Lesson 15 Doing Desirable Deeds

1. Tell about a time when you blessed someone anonymously.
2. Tell how you felt when you did something for someone else anonymously.
3. Tell how you feel when someone goes out of their way to do something nice for you.

Lesson 16 Choices and Consequences

1. Which life is more real – this earthly one or our eternal one? Explain.
2. How are God's curses used to bless us?

Lesson 17 Getting What You Give

1. Describe the difference between grace and mercy and tell what they saved you from and to.
2. Talk about the people that you honor and dishonor. Give each other the opportunity to respond.
3. Practice reciting your memorized verses.

Lesson 18 Wisdom – Perfect Prize

1. If an unbeliever cannot be truly wise, then is wisdom more about our actions here on earth or our future in heaven?
2. Jesus gives us wisdom to live this life and to prepare for eternity. How can wisdom prepare us for eternity?
3. Recite Proverbs 1:1-8 to a parent or teacher.

Lesson 19 Superb Scriptures

1. What does following God's Word mean in your life?
2. What changes do you need to make so that God's Word is a priority in each day?

Lesson 20 Working out a World View

1. How often must each of us choose to not enter the path of the wicked?
2. How can we avoid even entering the path of wickedness? What influences do you have in your life that you must guard against so that you won't enter the path of wickedness?
3. Discuss the world view questions from today's lesson.

Lesson 21 Heart Health

1. What thoughts has Satan put into your mind that you have chosen to believe?
2. How can you tell if a thought is your own, Satan's, or God's?
3. Explain Archbishop Leighton's quote and apply to your own life.

Lesson 22 Scintillating Sin

1. When sin entices us what should we remember?
2. What sin do you have a tendency towards or had a tendency towards in the past?
3. How is it more rewarding to choose not to commit this sin rather to give in to it. What are the rewards?

Lesson 23 Contentment or Covetousness

1. Practice reciting Proverbs 3:1-12.
2. What do you think are acceptable boundaries physically in a boy/girl relationship before marriage?
3. What are some standards that you can put into practice to keep from being tempted physically while with a member of the opposite sex? (ex. Always be where others can see you.)
4. What type of things do you covet?
5. Were you able to come up with 24 things that you are grateful for? If not see if mom or dad can help you finish the list.

Lesson 24 Sneaky Snares

1. Why, do you think, God is against surety?
2. How is a half-truth a whole lie?
3. What sins of the tongue do you struggle with?
4. Recite aloud Proverbs 3:1-12.

Lesson 25 Industrious Industry

1. Why is work good for your physical health? Your mental health? Your emotional health?
2. What type of work do you like to do best?
3. What chores can you offer to do around the house that you are not currently doing

Lesson 26 Fooleries of a Fool

1. Are your words to your parents bringing life or death? To your siblings?
2. Which of these sins has become a habit for you?
3. Are you going to commit to not doing that which is an abomination to God?

Lesson 27 Directing Discipline
1. How is being a Christian like a soldier?
2. How is being a Christian like an athlete?
3. How is being a Christian like a farmer?
4. Which of these metaphors challenges you the most?
5. Recite Proverbs 3:1-14 aloud.

Lesson 28 Leading Lust
1. Try to not think of the number 7.
2. Now that I said that, that is probably all that you can think about. Now think about the number 21. Are thinking about 7 anymore?
3. Our minds can only think on one thing at a time. When you are tempted by the things of this world, what verse of Scripture can you meditate on to keep your mind focused on God?

Lesson 29 New Nature
1. If you are born again, you are no longer a caterpillar, but a butterfly. Are you soaring in the clouds or still trying to get up off the ground?
2. Why should we who are forgiven from our sins, no longer to live in sin?
3. God is like a father, only perfect. That makes you His son or daughter. How does God respond to His children's sin?

Lesson 30 Proverbial Puzzle
1. Share a time when the character of Jesus showed you wisdom through a situation.

Lesson 31 and 32 Unfailing Foundation / Wise Words
1. If someone chooses not to believe in the truth of the Bible does that make the Bible not true?
2. Are there absolute truths?
3. Name some of these absolute truths.
4. Recite Proverbs 3:1-16 aloud.

Lesson 33 Illumined Inspiration
1. What are you doing now that you think God is using to equip you for some future work?
2. Share your personal Bible study plan with a parent or teacher.

Lesson 34 Comparing Character
1. Why does the foolish woman look to trap the righteous and not the foolish?
2. Does Satan attack unbelievers or believers more?
3. Discuss the wise and foolish charts.

Lesson 35 Receiving Reproof

1. When you were little and knew that you had done something that you shouldn't have done, did you fear your mom or dad?
2. When you drive over the speed limit do you fear the policeman sitting on the corner?
3. When you sin, do you fear God?
4. Recite Proverbs 3:1-26.

Lesson 36 and 37 Creating a New Creature / Freedom from Shame

1. When we were born again, we put on a new nature. How often do we need to put this nature on?
2. Does freedom in Christ mean that now you can do whatever you want to? Paul says that as sinners we were slaves to sin, but now we should be slaves to righteousness.

Lesson 38 Freedom from Shame

1. Does a Christian have any reason for shame from past or present actions?
2. As a prince or princess should we become haughty and selfish? Serving and graceful?
3. Work together to make a prayer box. Use any box such as a Kleenex box and decorate it. When you have something that you need to give to God, write it on a piece of paper and put it in the box. If you start worrying about this matter or trying to figure it out, take the piece of paper out of the box, pray, and place it into God's hands again by putting it back into the box.

Lesson 39 Comparing Characters

1. Give a speech using the paper that you wrote today.
2. Recite Proverbs 3:1-16 aloud.

Part 2 (Topical)

Lesson 40 Right Relationship with God

1. What is the difference between knowing about Abraham Lincoln and knowing Abraham Lincoln?
2. What is the difference between knowing about God and knowing God?
3. Pray for someone that you know that knows about God, but needs to know Him personally.

Lesson 41 Now what?

1. What is one chore or task that you have a hard time doing heartily as unto the Lord?
2. What praise song might you sing while doing this task that would make it more enjoyable?
3. Is God more interested in our getting our tasks done or our heart attitude as we do it?

Lesson 42 Feeding Frenzy

1. The temple in Jerusalem was an exquisite structure. It was overlaid in gold. How important was this building to the Jewish worshipper?
2. Is your body an exquisite dwelling place for the Lord? Why or why not.
3. What could you do to make your body a worthy dwelling place for the Holy Spirit?

Lesson 43 Poisonous Pursuits

1. Do you wish to be in authority some day?
2. Those in authority shouldn't drink alcohol or do drugs Why do you think this is?
3. Explain the quote, "What the parents do in moderation, the children will do in excess."
4. Give some positive and negative examples of this.

Lesson 44 Powerful Pride

1. In what areas or relationships do you battle pride?
2. How can you overcome this pride?
3. Are you willing to give it a try?
4. Recite Proverbs 3:1-20 to a parent or teacher.

Lesson 45 Perverted Pride

1. What is your self-esteem based upon?
2. What should your self-esteem be based upon?
3. How does this help you to avoid pride?

Lesson 46 Honoring Humility

1. Ask each other how you respond when life squeezes you.
2. How do you compare to each of the definitions of humility?

Lesson 47 Humble Heart

1. If we boast, what should we boast in? (Jeremiah 9:23)
2. In what areas of life are you tempted to boast about yourself?

Lesson 48 Perfect Parents

1. Ask your parents if they feel like you honor them. Discuss ways that you can honor them.
2. If we can't respect our parents, can we still honor them?
3. List some things that you are grateful for about your parents.

Lesson 49 Perfect Parent

1. How important is it to God that we honor our parents?
2. If someone does not honor their parents they are worthy of death according to Romans 1:28-32. Why do you think that is?
3. Recite Proverbs 3:1-22 aloud.

Lesson 50 Money Motivation

1. How important is money to you?
2. Do you put your trust in riches or God?
3. Are you rich and don't need God or poor and always worrying about where your next dollar will come from?
4. How can you begin to have a proper attitude about money?

Lesson 51 More Money

1. What heart condition should we learn in regards to money?
2. Do you expect things to go well and blame God when they go wrong or do you expect things to go wrong and praise God when they go right?
3. Who is the god of this world? Who wins in the end?
4. Are you content in whatever circumstance life finds you in?

Lesson 52 Wily Wealth

1. What are your basic needs?
2. Has God provided for your needs?
3. Tell of a time when God unexpectedly provided more than your needs.

Lesson 53 Excellent Economy

1. How might you give to the poor? (Not Mom and Dad's money, but your own).
2. Are you responsible for what someone does with that which you gave them?

Lesson 54 Money Matters

1. What is the heart issue behind false balances? Give an example that you have come across about false measurements.
2. What is the heart issue in usury?
3. What is the heart issue in borrowing? Give an example of how borrowing turned out to be a bad idea in your life.
4. Recite Proverbs 3:1-24 out loud.

Lesson 55 Believable Budget

1. Ask Mom or Dad to see their budget or have them outline it for you.
2. Go over your budget with Mom or Dad and ask for suggestions.

Lesson 56 History of Work Habits

1. Do you tend to be a workaholic or do you tend to avoid work as much as possible?
2. What motivates you to work hard?
3. Are you more valuable in God's estimation if you work hard or not?

Lesson 57 Worthwhile Work

1. Are you successful at making a short term work plan and accomplishing it?
2. What is your long term work plan? Does it include college, a trade school, apprenticing?
3. Discuss your ideas with a parent.

Lesson 58 Willing Worker

1. Are you an excuse maker?
2. What's the most creative excuse you ever made up or heard?
3. What area do you need to become more diligent in?

Lesson 59 Work and Wealth

1. Have you ever felt that you did not have enough faith because God did not seem to answer your prayer?
2. What three answers might a parent or God give if you ask for something?
3. Describe a time when God told you no or to wait.

Lesson 60 Work and Welfare

1. Are you tithing faithfully?
2. How might you give above your tithe?
3. Should we discern and treat differently the poor and the lazy poor? How might you treat each group to give the best help?
4. Recite Proverbs 3:1-26 aloud.

Lesson 61 – 63 Wise Words I, II, III

1. What sin of the tongue stands out most to you?
2. Why is this sin? How does it go against who God is?

Lesson 64 Wordy Words

1. Share your paper with your Mom or Dad.

Lesson 65 Perfect Performance

1. What is the relationship between the tongue and the heart?
2. What is the relationship between knowledge and the tongue?
3. If someone is having a hard time taming their tongue, what should be their approach to getting it under control?

Lesson 66 Last Word on Words

1. What areas of your life are you willing to tell a lie about?
2. Does lying come easily for you?
3. Is any lying justifiable?
4. Recite Proverbs 18:21 to a parent or a teacher.

Lesson 67 Ruinous Rage

1. What is your anger level?
2. Do you tend to confront the things that make you angry or repress your anger and hurt?
3. Practice some pretend situations that would make you angry and role play aggressive behavior and assertive behavior. This could be done as a whole family or class. Take turns coming up with scenarios.

Practical Proverbs

Lesson 68 Acting Out Anger

1. How do you grieve the hurts of your life?
2. How full or empty is your emotional bucket?
3. What pulls your train – your emotions or God's Word?
4. Recite Proverbs 3:1-26 for review.

Lesson 69 Fulfilling Forgiveness

1. Is there anyone that you need to forgive?
2. What debt will you have to forgive in order to forgive this person?
3. How much did God forgive you?
4. What excuses do you give for not forgiving?

Lesson 70 Bitter Battle

1. Which of these excuses have you used?

Lesson 71 Forgiveness Finished

1. What inaccurate meanings of forgiveness did you hold as true?
2. Are you going to choose to forgive?

Lesson72 Responsible Rearing

1. What are some of your natural bents?
2. What is your learning style?
3. How have you learned to compensate for your learning weaknesses?

Lesson 73 Totally Together

1. Who do you like to spend your time with?
2. Who might you invite to get together as a group not as couples but as individuals that have the same values as you do?
3. How is this plan different than most teenagers?
4. How is this plan different than the way that you have been approaching dating?
5. Are you willing to pray about this method and give it a try?

Lesson 74 Realistic Relationship

1. Share your list of things you will look for in a spouse from yesterday's lesson with your mom or dad.
2. What might someone have to give up to be a worker at home?
3. What might someone gain by being a worker at home?

Lesson 75 For Guys

1. Knowing these requirements to be a Godly husband, are you ready for marriage?
2. What do you cherish?
3. Are you able to cherish a person instead?

Lesson 76 For Girls

1. Is it wrong to be beautiful and to enhance your looks with make up or pretty clothes?
2. What should be your first priority in preparing yourself for marriage?
3. Are you a French horn or a trumpet?
4. Are you a hand tool or an electrical tool?

Lesson 77 Gracious Girls

Girls:

1. Are you a contentious woman?
2. If your answer to #1 is yes, what are you going to do to change that?
3. Is it okay to be contentious during your period?

Boys:

1. Do you know a contentious woman?
2. How do you feel in her presence?
3. Do you find yourself acting like a Godly man when you are with a contentious woman?

Lesson 78 Wise Woman

Girls:

1. Which of these actions seems hard for you to accomplish?
2. Choose a couple of these characteristics and decide to work on becoming ready for these tasks.

Boys: Begin praying for a Godly wife now and decide what your responsibilities will be. A woman will love a man that helps clean, encourages her work, and appreciates her crafts.

Lesson 79 Woman's Work and Worth

1. Have you called your mother blessed? Now would be a good time.
2. Pray with your parent for a Godly spouse.
3. What actions or words constitute abuse? Decide now that you will never engage in such behavior.
4. Last time. Recite Proverbs 3:1-26 aloud.

Lesson 80 God is....

1. Choose a couple of God's names and share how He has shown Himself faithful in these areas in your life.

Practical Proverbs

Introduction

What is wisdom? There is the wisdom of the ages, Biblical wisdom, wise sayings, wise cracks, and wise guys. But where do we find true wisdom? Is there a universal, absolute wisdom? Is wisdom knowledge? Understanding? Application? Or maybe all three?

Wisdom has to do with choices: On what to base our choices, understanding the consequences of our choices, weighing our choices. Choices about life, relationships, money, religion, duties, and even what to wear or eat and when, with whom, and how long.

Proverbs is a book of wisdom written by the wisest man that ever lived according to God. It is a great place to start a treasure hunt as you search for nuggets of wisdom. Along the way you will learn about yourself, your friends, your family, and your God.

To understand wisdom, you must also look at its opposite: foolishness. What are the characteristics and results of foolish choices? Of wise choices? Do your choices impact only the immediate? Or could a bad choice haunt you for a very long time?

This book is broken up into two sections. The first section will look at the Book of Proverbs found in the Bible and its history, its author, and its intended audience. You will define some words so that we are talking about the same things, and you will fill out a chart contrasting wisdom and foolishness.

The second part of the book will help you to apply what you have learned. You will learn about topics that are relevant to your life today and file away God's wisdom, proverb by proverb.

My prayer for you is that you will gain not only knowledge about wisdom, but wisdom on how to apply it to your life, that you may desire God's choices for each decision that will come up in your future, and that you will grow closer to God who loves you and has a plan and a purpose for your life.

Definitely Different Definitions

Lesson 1

When someone says the word "dog" to you, what comes to mind? Do you think of a miniature schnauzer, a golden retriever, a black lab, a beagle or some other kind of dog? Do you feel threatened or think it's cute? Do you imagine hours of pleasure running on the beach with man's best friend or are you curled up with your favorite pet on the couch watching TV?

Any word has the capacity to bring to our minds a lot of different images based upon our own experiences or interactions with the subject. To a Christian the word "God" should bring praise and anticipation, but to others who practice other religions "God" is to be feared and appeased. So, before we begin, we need to have the same working definitions for a few of the words that we will find in the book of Proverbs.

The first word is wisdom. When you think of wisdom do you think of King Solomon justly judging between the two women who brought a baby before him asking him to decide which woman was the real mother? (1 Kings 3:16-28). Do you think of your dad or grandfather who taught you about life? Maybe a teacher took time and interest in you and you think he/she had a lot of wisdom. Can wisdom be attained or is it something that we are born with and can be scored like our IQ?

Write what reminds you of wisdom. ______________________________________

____

The American Heritage Dictionary of the English Language defines wisdom as "Understanding of what is true, right, or lasting." And, "Common sense; good judgment."

As Christians we go one step deeper and define wisdom as "Understanding what is true, right, or lasting according to God and His Word, the Bible." And, "Using Biblical truths as the basis for good judgment."

We will use this working definition of wisdom: "The ability to judge correctly and use our knowledge to avoid trouble, solve problems, reach goals, and succeed in life based upon God's principles."

Mark the following that would be defined as wisdom.

_____1. Learning the names of the constellations
_____2. Knowing that lying is wrong and choosing to be truthful
_____3. Knowing what is for dinner
_____4. Saying no to harmful drugs
_____5. Finding joy in spending time with God

Hopefully you marked numbers 2, 4, and 5.

Our next word is Knowledge. You can tell from the above exercise that knowing is not the same as wisdom. Knowledge is having the facts. We should know the facts before we make a judgment or choice, but knowing is just the first step towards wisdom. If wisdom is based on making choices based on God's Word, I had better learn what God's Word says. Once I know what God would have me to do or how He would have me respond, then I can apply wisdom.

Proverbs was written by King Solomon so that his son would, "Know wisdom and instruction." Proverbs 4:13 says: "Take hold of instruction; let her not go. Guard her, for she is your life." Instruction is knowledge gained from someone who is more knowledgeable. Instruction is putting information in order; preparing, teaching, arranging, and building up information so it can be utilized. Again, instruction, like knowledge is a precursor of wisdom. Instruction is gained by taking the Word of God and learning how it can be applied; knowing how others have used God's words and principles, and how God honored that obedience in their lives.

To have wisdom then, first we need to know and then we need instruction – how to apply it. Wisdom is evident when we take what we know and apply it to our situation, our problem, our goals, our lives.

Go back through today's lesson and write a definition for each of these words:

1. Wisdom:

2. Knowledge:

3. Instruction:

Begin memorizing the working definition of wisdom: "The ability to judge correctly and use our knowledge to avoid trouble, solve problems, reach goals, and succeed in life based upon God's principles."

Determining Definitions

Lesson 2

Knowing is the facts.
Instruction is the learning about the facts and their use.
Wisdom is applying the facts by making right choices.

Proverbs was also written to Solomon's son that he might "...perceive the words of understanding." Proverbs 1:2

To perceive is to discern. What is discernment? Discernment is being able to distinguish between good and evil, leading us to act with wisdom.

If we are to act wisely, we had better know what is right, true, and lasting. There are several types of discernment. Where someone might be good at discerning people, someone else might be better at discerning current situations, and someone else might be good at discerning future plans and ideas. My husband has a keen ability to know if someone is telling the truth and working with integrity. One of my sons is very good at discerning God's will in his life for each decision, and another son is great with discerning whether a particular plan will be the best or if another ought to be considered.

The neat thing about discernment is that it can be developed. Hebrew 5:14 says that "...solid food is for the mature, who because of practice have their senses trained to discern good and evil." Solid food is referring to deeper understanding and application of God's Word. Discernment is like a muscle, the more we use it the stronger it becomes. Once again, however, we find that discernment is based on knowledge – knowledge of God's Word. You need to be reading the Bible. Throughout this course, you will be encouraged to develop a stronger prayer life and to be in the Word more and more. Remember knowledge, then instruction, then discernment and wisdom.

Our next word is subtilty. Another reason for the writing of Proverbs is "To give subtilty to the simple." (Proverbs 1:4). The American Heritage Dictionary of the English Language defines subtilty as "Able to make fine distinctions". Another word for subtilty is Prudence. Prudence is being modest and proper. Often someone who dresses with modesty or has strict rules about where he/she can go and what he/she can do is called a prude. That is the same root word used here. The prude is careful about his conduct, because he/she can make a fine distinction between right and wrong. To those around him who have looser rules and don't understand God's standards, he is a prude, but to God he is being prudent.

Who are the simple in Proverbs 1:4? One who is simple (naïve)has no knowledge, or having received knowledge, has refused to apply it to his own life with wisdom. This is different than someone who cannot learn. Do you know someone who is simple-minded? Are you simple-minded in some areas? I am very simple-minded when it comes to understanding the mechanical workings of a car. I don't know. I don't want to know. I just put gas in it and it runs. This does not get me into trouble because

my husband understands cars and keeps me out of trouble. On the other hand, if something happened to my husband and I had to take responsibility for my car, then it could be very costly to remain simple-minded about car mechanics. I would need to seek knowledge and instruction on the care of the automobile.

> What are you simple-minded about? Does this cause problems?
>
> ____
>
> ____

At other times being simple-minded is not acceptable. We should not remain simple-minded about personal cleanliness, social graces, acceptable language, and most importantly – God's design for our lives. God is the author of creation. As the creature, we should go to Him to find out the rules of our existence. He holds the playbook, the manual, and even the end of the story in His hands. "Proverbs can give subtilty to the simple." (Proverbs 1:4) It can teach us what we don't know – what we should know. I wouldn't want to go to war without going through boot camp where I can learn how to shoot and strategize to come home alive. Proverbs is a Christian boot camp. In it is the wisdom of the Lord God our Maker. Within its words are life and success and victory and eternal life.

Just one more word to define for now – Discretion. Discretion is thinking about and applying wisdom before it comes out in words or actions. In other words, think before you speak and sometimes think and don't speak. Apply wisdom to your own life, live it out and then others will be open to hearing what you have to say. Discretion means knowing when to speak and when to be silent.

Go back through today's lesson and write a definition for each of these words:

1. Discernment:

2. Subtilty:

3. Simple-minded:

4. Discretion:

Be sure that you are memorizing the working definition of wisdom from lesson one.

Detailing Definitions

Lesson 3

Okay – Time for a pop quiz. Try it without looking back, then if you need to look back for a few clues go ahead. There won't be a grade.

1. Proverbs was written by
    a. King David
    b. King Solomon
    c. Jesus
    d. Confucius

2. Wisdom is the ability to judge correctly and use our knowledge to avoid trouble, solve problems, reach goals, and succeed in life based upon ____________ principles.

3. According to the above definition what must be acquired before wisdom can be obtained?
    a. Experience
    b. Age
    c. Love
    d. Knowledge

4. How do we get knowledge about God's wisdom?
    a. Pray
    b. Read the Bible
    c. Listen to good biblical teachers
    d. Memorize Scripture
    e. All of the above

5. Instruction is gained by taking the __________________ ________ ____________ and learning how it can be applied; knowing how others have used God's words and principles and how God honored that in their lives.

6. True or False. There is only one type of discernment? _________________

7. True or False. Discernment is a gift that you either have or don't have; it can't be gained. ____________________

8. How can we get discernment?
    a. It's a gift.
    b. We have to exercise.
    c. Only old people can get it.

9. True or False. We should make fun of someone who is a "prude."

____

10. True or False. We should have subtilty and, thus, we should be a prude.

____

11. True or False. Sometimes it's okay to be simple-minded _________________

12. It's okay to be simple-minded about:
   a. God's Words
   b. Automobile engines
   c. God's plan for you
   d. Wisdom

13. True or False. Discretion says that if I know the answer I should always belt it right out. ________________________

How did you do? Are you a little wiser or do you just know more? _________________

Maybe you are not as naïve and, perhaps, you are a little more discerning.

Read Proverbs 1:1-7 and fill in the blanks.

The proverbs of __________________ the son of David, king of Israel;
To know ___________________ and ____________________;
to ____________________ the words of _____________________________,
To receive the _______________________of ____________________,
justice, and judgment, and equity;
To give ________________________ to the ____________________,
to the young man ______________________ and _________________________.
A wise man will hear, and will increase in learning;
and a man of _____________________________ shall attain unto wise counsels:
To understand a proverb, and the interpretation;
the words of the wise, and their dark sayings.
The fear of the Lord is the beginning of ______________________:
but fools despise ________________________ and ________________________.

Answers to quiz: 1.) b 2.) God's 3.) d 4.) e 5.) Word of God 6.) False 7.) False 8.) b 9.) False 10.) True 11.) True 12.) b 13.) False

Daring David

Lesson 4

Solomon is the author of Proverbs. Solomon got his wisdom from God. We will read more about him in the next couple of days. But Solomon's dad, King David, also learned wisdom from God and through his own experiences. Today's lesson will focus on David and the most important lessons of consequences, repentance, and choices.

For this lesson you will need: a small piece of wood
2-3 nails (any size)
a hammer.

Read the following, follow directions, and answer the questions that follow.

God had established Israel in the land of Canaan. God ruled the people through judges and prophets that He appointed, but the people wanted a king. (Read 1 Samuel 8:7-9)

In 1 Samuel 8:7-9, whom had Israel rejected: God or Samuel?

____

In 1 Samuel 8:7-9, what was Israel's great sin? ______________________

God reluctantly consented and had His prophet Samuel anoint Saul as king. Saul reigned 32 years over Israel, but he sinned before the Lord. God sent Samuel to tell him a prophecy of what was to come. (Read 1 Samuel 13:14). This prophecy was fulfilled in David.

What characteristics would the new king have?

____

____

David was just a shepherd boy when Samuel anointed him king. (Read 1Samuel 16:7, 12-13)

Man looks at the outer appearance of men, but what does God look at?

____

When David was anointed king, what came upon him mightily? ____________

Before David took the throne as king, however, he first became a musician in the king's court soothing Saul's moods and evil spirit. (Read 1 Samuel 16:17-19, 23)

List the six attributes used to describe David.

1. 4.
2. 5.
3. 6.

He also became the king's armor bearer, the victor over Goliath, a strong warrior, the king's son's best friend, and the king's son-in-law. He is chased by the king, hunted down by the king's men and given opportunity to kill the king. But David denied himself because he recognized that the king was God's anointed. God watched over David through these years of treachery, betrayal, and battles. After Saul was slain and David was finally made king, God made a covenant with him through Nathan the prophet. (Read 2 Samuel 7:8-17.)

What does God attribute David's success to?

____

____

Who is prophesied of in 2 Samuel 7: 12, 13, 16? _________________________

David responded with praise and humility. (Read 2 Samuel 7:18-29)

Whom did David ask God to magnify?

____

David, however, soon fell to temptation and committed adultery and murder. God again spoke to David through Nathan. (Read 2 Samuel 12:1-12)

Who was the rich man in this parable? __________________________

David repented, (Read 2 Samuel 12:13 and Psalm 51), but we see the consequences of his sin in 2 Samuel 12:14, 18a and Psalm 38.

What were some of the consequences of David's sin?

____

____

God forgave David and blessed him with another child – Solomon (Read 2 Samuel 12:24-25) also known as Jedidiah which means "Beloved of the Lord".

Take your piece of wood and hammer a few nails into it (far enough to make a hole, but able to be easily removed). The wood represents our lives. The nails are sins that we commit and allow to come into our lives. A sin is anything we do that is against God's law. When we repent, our sins are forgiven (1 John 1:9). They are thrown as far as the east is from the west (Psalm 103:12-13). Remove the nails and lay them out of sight. What is left in the wood? These holes represent the consequences that follow our sin. Even when God removes our sins, we must live with the scars and results. Jesus gives us victory even over all of this (Romans 8:28).

David praised God (2 Samuel 22-23:7) and Solomon reigned after David's death and brought Israel to its Golden Age.

David claims God as whose rock, fortress, deliverer, God, refuge, shield, horn of salvation, stronghold, and savior? ____

God can be your rock, fortress, deliverer, God, refuge, shield, horn of salvation, stronghold, and savior, too.

Listen now to David's last words to Solomon: (Read 1 Kings 2:2-4).

If Solomon keeps God's laws, statutes, commandments, and testimonies, what will be Solomon's reward? ____

What will be his sons' rewards? ____
____
____

More on King Solomon tomorrow.

Good job. God always welcomes a broken and contrite heart (Psalm 51:17). Repentance is the beginning of a long and successful relationship with our Creator and the Lover of Our Souls.

Fill in the blanks about wisdom:

Wisdom is the ability that enables us to use our ________________ to avoid ____________________, solve _________________________, reach ___________, and ______________________ in life – all from _________________ perspective.

Sagacious Solomon

Lesson 5

Let's find out about David's son, Solomon, the writer of Proverbs.

Read 1 Kings 2:12 and 4:20-28. We find that during Solomon's reign, Israel reaches its height of power, land, riches, reputation, and peace. Let's find out why.

Read 1 Kings 3:1-15, 4:29-34.

In 1 Kings 3:3 what was Solomon's motivation for obeying God?

____

In 1 Kings 3:9, what did Solomon ask of God?____________________

What was God's response? ______________________________

____

What was the condition God put upon His promise? ________________

____

Solomon's greatest earthly accomplishment was the building of a temple for God in Israel. Up to this time, God had dwelt in the midst of His people in a tent, a tabernacle. The presence of God rested upon the Ark of the Covenant kept within an inner room of the tabernacle called the Holy of Holies. Only the high priest was allowed in the presence of the ark, and then only once a year after many sacrifices. He would make a yearly sacrifice on the ark to God for the atonement of Israel's sins. (Atonement is a covering up of – the sacrifices covered up their sins.)

In 1 Kings 8:10-11, we see that God enters Solomon's temple to dwell or *tabernacle* there. At the dedication of this magnificent new temple, we find Solomon's heart as he prays to God. (Read 1 Kings 8:22-53).

In 1 Kings 8:22-24, Solomon first offers ____________ to God. Then he states that God will keep His ______________ and ____________ with those that walk before God with all their heart.

In 1 Kings 8:40, how were the people to respond to God's just judgments and mercy? ______________________________________

Solomon then blessed the people (Read 1 Kings 8:55-61).

In 1 Kings 8:60, why was it so important that the people walk in God's ways?

____

How much of our heart does God want? ____________________________________

God responds to Solomon with a promise and a warning (1 Kings 9:1-9).

In 1 Kings 9:4-5, what are the conditions of God's promise? ___________________
____

In 1 Kings 9:6-7, what would lead God to cut Israel off from the land and to destroy the nation? ____

However, we find that even Solomon, with God's wisdom, falters and falls (Read 1 Kings 11:1-6).

What was Solomon's sin? ____

He repents, but not before he, too, is told the consequences of his sins. (Read 1 Kings 11:9-13).

What are the consequences of his sin? _____________________________________
____

The book of Ecclesiastes is an autobiography of Solomon's life. He ends this great book with great words of wisdom. (Read Ecclesiastes 12:9-14.)

In Ecclesiastes 12:9-14, what did Solomon conclude at the end of his life?
____
____
____

Your definition for wisdom is due tomorrow. Make sure you can recite it out loud.

Spectacular Salvation

Lesson 6

Before we continue, we must look at the fulfillment of God's promise to David in order to keep in balance God's laws and judgments and God's love, grace, mercy, and provision. Proverbs was written before Christ, and the Jews were under the law of God at this time. Therefore, Proverbs leans heavily towards God's laws and we must guard against being legalistic as we acquire wisdom and discernment. We will do this throughout the study by studying verses in the New Testament that reveal God's forgiveness and promises through Christ Jesus.

There are hundreds of prophecies in the Old Testament that are fulfilled through the life, resurrection, and ascension of our Lord Jesus. Many of these prophecies surround God's promise to David that he would have an heir on the throne forever. This promise is given again in Isaiah 9:7. It is fulfilled as we read Luke 1:32-33. David's throne is everlasting as Jesus reigns at the right hand of God and will eventually rule over His eternal kingdom. Much of Psalms is attributed to David's pen and includes prophecies of Jesus' life. Prophecies are a fascinating study, but for this study we must move on.

We saw in David's and Solomon's lives, the inability to walk perfectly before God keeping His commandments, statutes, and testimonies. And yet, without a wholehearted devotion to God, we are promised His curses, not His blessings of abundance. Here is where the marvelous, glorious, wonderful provision of God through Jesus comes in.

Romans 3:10 claims that, "…there is none righteous, no, not one." Romans 3:23 continues that "…all have sinned, and come short of the glory of God." Our God is holy (set apart and perfect). We cannot stand in His presence and have sin in our lives. Therefore, from the beginning of time, a blood sacrifice was required for the "covering up" of our sins. Romans 6:23a states that, "The wages of sin is death…" We have all sinned (literally meaning that we have "missed the mark") and therefore, we all deserve death (eternal separation from God). But the rest of that verse brings hope and joy. Romans 6:23 says, "The gift of God is eternal life through Jesus Christ our Lord.".

Jesus was born of woman, but not of man and, therefore, did not inherit man's sinful nature or tendency passed down to all mankind through Adam. Jesus lived a perfect life, walking on this earth for approximately 32 years without sinning even once. He didn't sin and therefore, He didn't deserve death. He, however, allowed Himself to be crucified so that His blood would cover each of our sins. He was my (and your) substitute. He rose again on the third day and later ascended into heaven to sit at God's right hand. Now, when God sees me, He doesn't see my sin – it is "covered up" by Christ's blood. And what must I do to be saved? Romans 10:9-10 says, "That if thou shalt confess with thy mouth the Lord Jesus, and shalt believe in thine heart that God hath raised him from the dead, thou shalt be saved."

It is important that we really understand this and can explain it to others. Fill in the following *Romans' Road* with the verses in Romans in the order that can lead one to salvation.

Put these verses in order as you would tell someone how to get to God.

Romans 6:23b
Romans 10:9-10
Romans 3:23
Romans 6:23a
Romans 3:10

Ask God to show you a friend or family member that you can share this good news with and then do it.

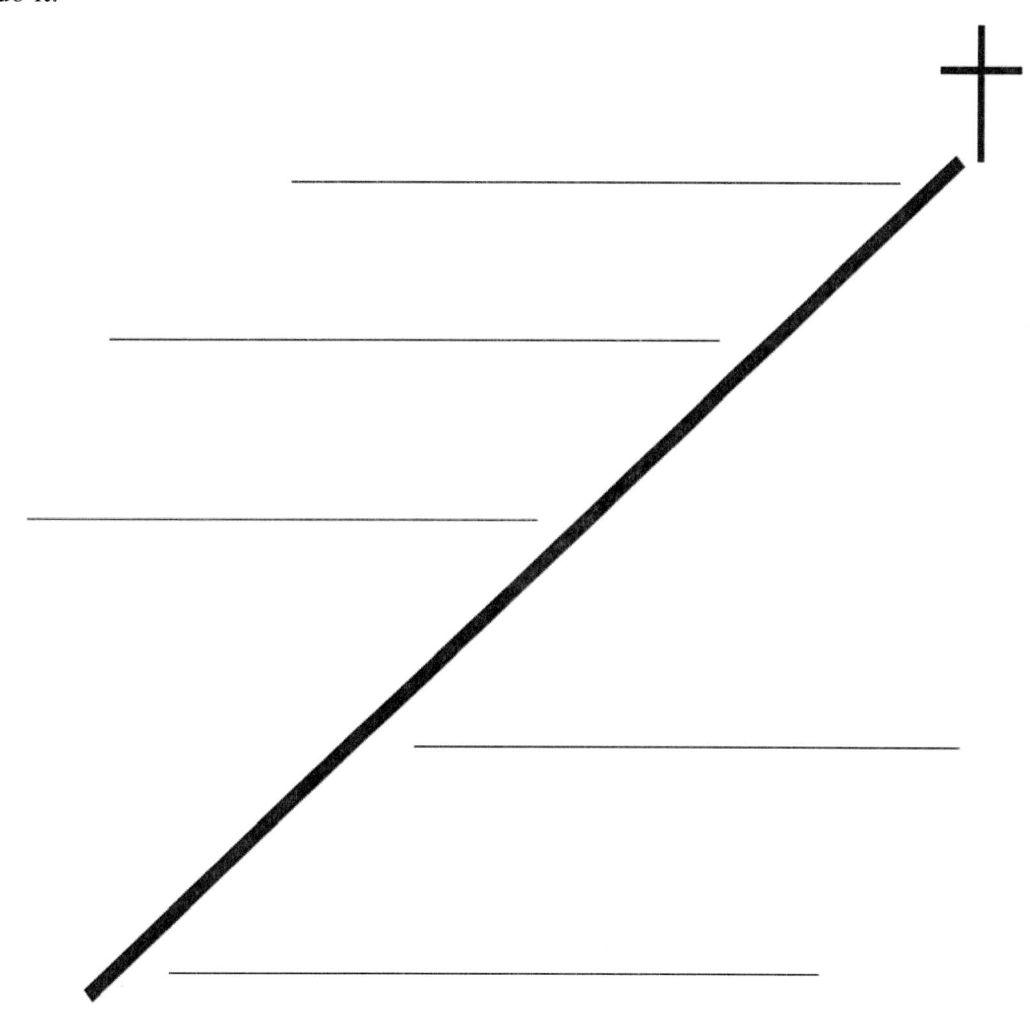

Begin memorizing Proverbs 1:5.

Respected Rules

Lesson 7

Noah Webster and George Washington both wrote notebooks full of rules to live by. These great men understood the necessity of giving themselves some boundaries for their behavior that would provide their lives with stability and allow them to reach their goals.

Some of George Washington's self-enforced rules are found in a small book called *Rules of Civility and Decent Behavior in Company and Conversation.* (Bedford, MA: Applewood Books, 1988). His first recorded rule is "Every action done in company ought to be some sign of respect to those that are present."

Some are common sense and others not so obvious. I especially like #9: "Spit not in the fire, not stoop low before it. Neither put your hands into the flames to warm them, nor set your feet upon the fire, especially if there be meat before it."

A very useful rule for those families with more than one child is # 70: "Reprehend not the imperfections of others, for that belongs to parents, masters, and superiors."

And, lastly, #110, "Labour to keep alive in your breast that little celestial fire called conscience."

Many people think of the Bible as a rulebook with a list of *don't's.* What they don't understand is that those *don't's* provide a hedge of protection. Just as a child is told, "Don't play in the street", and a teenager, "Don't smoke", the Biblical *don't's* keep us from harmful attitudes and actions that could scar us, maim us, or even kill us. God is not a *holy killjoy.* Just the opposite is true. He wants to bless us abundantly. He has preserved good things for His children. If we choose to live within His boundaries, He promises us peace, abundant life, and eternal life. He warns us, however, of the consequences of a life lived outside of His commands.

Read Romans 7:14-8:17 and list your top ten rules to live by:

1.

2.

3.

4.

5.

6.

7.

8.

9.

10.

Define:

COMMANDMENTS:

LAWS:

STATUTES:

TESTIMONIES:

Read Psalm 19:7-14 and fill in the following chart.

God's Word	Is what?	Accomplishing what?
1. The law of the Lord	perfect	converting the soul
2.		
3.		
4.		
5.		
6.		

Verse 10 continues to give worth to the Word of God – It is more desirable than gold and sweeter than honey. It accomplishes two things: it warns God's servant and brings great reward.

Wow! We can trust in God's Word, knowing that it will produce in us all that is its essence – perfection, sureness, righteousness, purity, cleanness, and truth.

Awesome Audience

Lesson 8

Now that we know who wrote the book of Proverbs, let us figure out to whom he wrote it. Who was Solomon's audience? Why did he take such pains to write it all down?

Look first at Proverbs 1:8-10. To whom was Solomon writing?

____

Take a green highlighter and highlight the words of your answer above in all of the following verses. Jot your answers down next to each verse. Then as we journey through Proverbs we will be reminded again and again to whom the book was written.

Proverbs 1:8	6:3
1:10	6:20
1:15	7:1
2:1	7:24
3:1	8:32
4:1	23:15
4:10	23:19
4:20	23:26
5:1	24:13
5:20	24:21
6:1	27:11

Now that we know to whom the book was written, let's dig deeper and discover why.

Let's start by reviewing Proverbs 1:2-7. It seems important to this writer dad that his audience (his son.) learn wisdom, instruction, discernment, and knowledge and be able to share it with others. The love of a father is the main motivator here. Solomon wanted to make sure that his son was equipped to handle all that life might throw at him, because he loved his son. I truly believe that God included it in His Book to us for exactly the same reason – He loves us and wants us to experience the best of life. He is a Father writing to His children.

Look at Proverbs 2:1-5. The ultimate end of a man's search is to discern the fear of the Lord and to discover the knowledge of God. Continuing on in verses 2:6-22, Solomon reveals why this is so important. God will be a shield to the upright, He will preserve the ways of His godly ones, He will deliver us from the way of evil, and then we will live in the land and remain in it – heaven forever!

The following verses tell us some of the other reasons that the author wrote these words for his son.

1:8-9 – ____

3:1 – ______________________________
3:4 – ______________________________
3:6 – ______________________________
3:8 – ______________________________
3:22 – ______________________________
3:23 – ______________________________
3:24 – ______________________________
4:6 – ______________________________
4:8 – ______________________________
4:10 – ______________________________
4:20 – ______________________________
6:22 – ______________________________
6:24 – ______________________________
7:5 – ______________________________
8:32 – ______________________________
22:18 – ______________________________
22:21 – ______________________________
23:15 – ______________________________
23:24-25 – ______________________________
24:14 – ______________________________

What promises! All based upon a father's love, a father's desire to see his son lead a long, successful, and satisfied life. Just as this earthly father desired these joys for his son, how much more our heavenly Father wants us to be blessed with His abundance.

Your green highlighter will be used throughout this study to highlight the motivation for the writing of the book. Go ahead and highlight in green Proverbs 1:2-9. Great job! Keep up the good work.

Keep working on proverbs 1:5.

Foolish Folly

Lesson 9

In the next several lessons, we will be looking at a Biblical fool and foolishness and a Biblical wise man and wisdom. These are the foundations of the book of Proverbs.

Let us first define a *Biblical fool*. We will draw our knowledge first from Psalm 14:1-3. It is interesting to note that these verses are repeated by Paul in Romans 3:10-12 to describe the state of man *under sin* before being reconciled unto Christ.

According to these verses what does a fool say in his heart? ____________________
____

After he has made this declaration, he then acts corruptly. Sins committed does not make us sinners, but rather our sin nature makes us sin, for Jesus said in Matthew 15:18,

"But those things which proceed out of the mouth come from the ________________; and they defile the man."

We will be highlighting verses in Proverbs in blue that tell us more about foolishness and fools. Keep in mind that as only Christ was perfect, we all have areas in our lives where we still act foolishly. The good news is that as we are made right in Jesus Christ, He convicts us of our foolish ways and helps us to overcome habits, ideas, and ways that are bound up in our old nature. If you notice a foolish action in Proverbs that you still need help with, put a star beside that verse and begin praying that God will help you be an overcomer.

Turn to Appendix A and you will find a chart entitled *Foolishness: Characteristics and Results*. As you add to this chart over the following weeks, you will get a very good picture of a fool and the consequences of his foolishness.

Read the following verses and decide if the information contained in them is a characteristic of a fool or a result of his foolishness. List them under the correct heading. They do not have to be across from each other according to the verses. Just start at the top and make a list, jotting down key words or phrases. The first one has been done for you.

Proverbs	1:7	
	1:11	1:19
	1:12	1:22
	1:13	1:29
	1:16	1:30
	1:18	1:32

Proverbs 1:5 should be memorized by tomorrow.

Faulty Foolishness

Lesson 10

You should have your wisdom definition completely memorized as well as Proverbs 1:5.

Tomorrow we will begin memorizing a long passage: Proverbs 3:1- 26. But don't panic. We will take it slowly, a little bit at a time and you will have the rest of the study to finish it up.

According to Jan Silvious in her book, *Foolproofing your Life*, (Random House, Inc. 2009), characteristics of a fool include the belief that he/she is always right, the use of anger to control, and trusting in his/her own heart. Throughout the book of Proverbs, we will see that a fool is easily taken in by sin and refuses to put it aside thus becoming a stumbling block for others. In Proverbs 1:10-19, we see that sin is enticing; it's fun for the moment. I love the verse in Hebrews that describes Moses' choices: Hebrews 11:25 says:

> "Choosing rather to suffer affliction with the people of God, than to enjoy the ____________________________ of sin for a ____________________________.
>
> His motive was pure as seen in verse 26: "Esteeming the reproach of Christ _________________riches than the treasures of Egypt; for he had respect unto the recompence of the reward."

And that's really what Proverbs (and life) is about. It's about choices and taking responsibility for our own choices. Sin, for the moment or season, can be pleasurable and fun. I won't deny that. That third and fourth piece of fudge are good until you get a stomachache and add another pound.

> But let us not forget that sin leads to _____________________ (Romans 6:23 and James 1:14-15).

The short term excitement is not worth the break in relationship between us and God or the consequences.

Proverbs uses the metaphor of an adulteress to personify sin, sinfulness, Satan's deceptions, and the results thereof. Read Proverbs 2:16-19, 5:3-6, 6:26-35, and 7:6-27.

This metaphor was also used continuously by God to describe the nation of Israel as her heart turned from Him to the gods and idols of other cultures. Jeremiah 3:1-3 is one of a myriad of references where God compares His beloved children to harlots and adulteresses. This comparison is not limited to sexual relationships only (although this is certainly involved in Israel's unfaithfulness). It applies to a heart condition of rebellion and self-gratification.

Moses teaches the Israelites in Deuteronomy 6:5 to "Love the Lord thy God with _________ thine heart, and with ________ thine soul, and with _________ thine might."

But the pleasures of sin were enticing and their hearts were drawn away by the allure of riches, lands, freedom from rules, and all other forms of easy living. As we saw with Solomon, this did not (and does not) satisfy.

The fool in Proverbs, likewise, is drawn to the adulteresses' home and allured into sensual pleasures, thus forfeiting all the blessings of God and godly living. You can't have it both ways. You must choose.

> Add to your chart (Appendix A) the characteristics of foolishness and its results found in Proverbs 2:16-19
> 5:3-6
> 6:26-35
> 7:6-27

Don't forget to highlight these verses in your Bible with your blue highlighter.

Using Jan Silvious' definition of a fool, write a paragraph of a time that you acted the part of a fool. Conclude with Deuteronomy 6:5 and how this could have prevented those foolish notions.

Wonderful Wisdom

Lesson 11

Let's turn to the uplifting, positive side of Proverbs and discuss wisdom. We are first introduced to wisdom in Proverbs 1:20-33. Read these verses.

In verses 20-23, is wisdom hiding and hard to find? ________________________

In verses 24-29, is wisdom hard to find? ________________________________

Our reaction to wisdom makes the difference. This reminds me of a verse, Matthew 7:7.

What does this verse say we need to do to find Jesus, the All Wise One?

____

James 1:5 also tells us to ask for wisdom and it will be given to us.

According to this verse to what extent will God give us wisdom? _____________

That's right, He will give it generously.

Proverbs 1:33 is a key to finding happiness in this life. Sometimes life seems overwhelming because of the evil in the world around us. Just read the front page of the newspaper or watch the evening news and you will find evil in all its forms. But we can rest in the fact that if we seek wisdom, then we

"Shall dwell ______________________,
and shall be quiet from fear of evil." (Proverbs 1:33)

Isaiah 30: 15 is a great verse to memorize and practice.

"In ____________________ and ______________ shall you be saved, in
________________________ and in _________________ shall be your strength."

Here in Proverbs 1, we find wisdom personified. She is actively seeking out those whose hearts will turn to her. This should not surprise us. A key to understanding wisdom is found in Proverbs 8:22-31. These verses describe wisdom as one who was with God before the beginning of time, who was a master craftsman even as God formed our world. Before there were depths, this wisdom was brought or born forth (verse 24).

This wisdom was manifested in the flesh as Jesus Christ. John 1:1-5 tells us that He was with God from the beginning and that all things came into being through Him. He is the only begotten of the Father (John 1:14). "For the Son of Man is come to seek and to save that which was lost." (Luke 19:10). It is inherent of God to want to call His children back to Himself and His life-giving laws. So wisdom seeks out those who will allow themselves to be drawn to her, those who will choose her paths.

Our response to wisdom is the dividing line.

According to Proverbs 2:6 where does wisdom come from?

____

Let's look again at Proverbs 1:20-33. Wisdom promises us that if we but turn to her (Jesus), that the Holy Spirit will be poured out upon us and He will make His words known to us. According to verse 33, we will live securely and be at ease from the dread of evil. However, verses 24-32 tells us what happens to those who refuse her generous and free offer.

What are the consequences of not looking for wisdom?

____

Proverbs 2:1-5 again reminds us that we must look for wisdom. In verse 2 we must,

"So that thou incline thine ear unto __________________, and apply thine ________ to understanding."
Verse 3 says, "If thou criest after ___________________________, and liftest up thy voice for ___________________________."
Verse 4 continues, "If thou ________________ her."
Then in verse 5, "Then shalt thou understand the fear of the Lord, and ________________________ the knowledge of God."

Once again we see that wisdom is not hidden if we seek her. God is not trying to make this difficult. He just requires that we be sincere and will look to Him for wisdom. Is God's wisdom different than that of man? Find the answer in 1Corinthians 1:18-31.

Write verse 25 here: ____
____
____

Proverbs 2:6-12a, 20-21 gives us a brief glance at what can be ours if we but "Love the Lord thy God with all thine heart, with all thine soul and with all thine might." (Deuteronomy 6:5)

List 12 things from these verses that are ours if we seek wisdom.

1.
2.
3.
4.
5.
6.
7.
8.
9.
10.
11.
12.

Mark Proverbs 1:20-21, 23, 33, 2:6-12, 20-21 in yellow for wisdom. Turn to Appendix B entitled *Wisdom: Characteristics and Results*. Begin filling in your chart with these verses:

Proverbs	1:23	2:10
	1:33	2:11
	2:7	2:12
	2:8	2:20
	2:9	2:21

Mark these and all wisdom verses with your yellow highlighter.

Start memorizing our long passage by getting down the first verse. Appendix C is a copy of these verses. I find that by drawing little pictures or symbols alongside of the words that I can memorize them better. Try it. For instance, draw a heart above the word heart in verse one.

Try Trusting

Lesson 12

Continue memorizing the first couple of verses of Proverbs 3. Try to have a good grasp of verses 1–4 in another three or four days.

Today's and tomorrow's lessons will hone in on the semester's memory verses: Proverbs 3:1-26. Proverbs 3 is a central passage to this incredible book. It contains the key to the mystery of how to live a godly life, what the blessings of that life are, an understanding of God's correction, the priority of wisdom and God in our lives, and even some practical advice. So let's get started.

Let's look first at this great mystery of how to live a godly life. There are people all over our world today and in every generation past looking, searching, and seeking for the way to God. Every major religion – Hinduism, Islam, Confucianism, Buddhism, etc., as well as the major cults: Mormonism, Jehovah Witnesses, New Age, etc. are all looking for what men must do to be saved. In each of these religions, the answer is within man's power. If one prays hard enough, witnesses enough, does enough good works, meditates enough, or even gives up enough, then he/she will reach *god.* Islam promises heaven to those who die killing their enemies – Christians and Jews.

Christianity is the only religion that stipulates that man's best is as filthy rags to God (Isaiah 64:6). Only in Christianity does one see, not man's work, but God's work – as Jesus walked upon earth without sin and then died as a substitute for all of our sins. His last words? "It is finished." We don't have to do anything else. Nothing more is required.

In Acts 16:30, some jailers asked Paul and Silas, "…what must I do to be saved?"

> Their reply was, "______________________on the Lord Jesus Christ, and thou shalt be saved…"

That was it – no religious rituals or magic words. Ephesians 2:8 reiterates the work of salvation as a gift of God. "For by grace are ye saved through faith; and that not of yourselves, it is the gift of God; not of works, lest any man should boast."

> Jesus, Himself, says, "I am the way, the truth, and the life; _______ ______________ cometh unto the Father, but by me." (John 14:6).

And God the Father states many times in the Old Testament that He desires not our sacrifices, but rather our hearts, broken and contrite before God. (Psalm 51:16)

So, back to Proverbs. Look at verses 3:5-6. Write these verses here: __________________
____
____

If we are believing in Jesus as Savior, but also as Lord, then we can trust in His promises, His provisions, His guidance, and direction and, in verses 11-12, His correction, reproof and discipline.

In Jeremiah 29:11, God proclaims His intentions. "For I know the thoughts that I think towards you; saith the Lord, thoughts of ________________, and not of evil, to give you an ______________________end."

We see from this that trusting in God is not a blind faith but rather faith in One who is able, who has the capacity to deliver, and who desires what is very best for us. We receive an understanding of God our Father from doing what Proverbs 3:1-4 commands – by knowing His Word, keeping His Word, memorizing His Word (binding it around your neck, writing them on the tablets of your heart). Then we open the channel of relationship and blessings between man and God. God desires not our works but our hearts. (Jeremiah 24:7, Deuteronomy 4:29). And to top it off, this life of trust is spent with the blessings of Jesus.

Let's see what blessings you can find in Proverbs 3:1-10. (I found 10.)

Wow! What a good and mighty God we serve!

Add the chapter 3:1-10 verses to your wisdom and foolishness charts. And highlight them the appropriate colors in your Bible. Continue to highlight verses throughout this curriculum – blue for foolishness and yellow for wisdom.

Continue memorizing the first couple of verses of Proverbs 3. Try to have a good grasp of verses 1–4 in another three or four days.

Daring Discipline

Lesson 13

Let's continue on with the rich wisdom of Proverbs 3. We'll begin by looking at verses 11-12. Read these verses. These are not easy verses, but, oh the blessing because even discipline is in God's character. Discipline definitely includes correction and punishment but also embraces the idea of loving guidance. Reproof is the reminder of the wrong and the way to correcting that wrong. Both can be gentle, or both may require punishment and/or a harsh attention-getting circumstance.

Let's take a minute and look at Deuteronomy. These passages are so foundational to understanding God's desire to bless, but also His right to discipline His people.
Read Deuteronomy 4:1-10.

In verses 1, 6, 10 – Why did God give the Israelites statutes and judgments?

____

____

Read Deuteronomy 4:11-20.

Verses 15 and 19 contain two warnings. What are they?

____

____

Read Deuteronomy 4:21-28.

Verse 24 describes God as a _______________ God.

We think of jealousy as a bad trait. But in this situation it is a wonderful characteristic of a holy God. God will not stand by and allow His followers to share their worship and devotion with false gods. He wants our whole hearts, not just a little bit. The Christian Romans who so often sacrificed their lives during the time of the Caesars did so not because of their worship of Jesus, but because of their exclusive worship of Jesus. The Romans wouldn't have minded if they had set their God up on the mantle along with the Roman gods, or if they had bowed to Jesus along with bowing to Caesar. But, the early Christians would bow and worship God and God alone, and so they were martyred.

Moses gives the Israelites a warning in verses 25-28. They will be guilty of what sin? ____

And what will be their punishment? ______________________________

____

Read Deuteronomy 4:29-39. Wow. What great promises. Verse 29 says that we can find God.

What must we do to find God?

____

Verse 30 prophesies that the people shall return to God and shall be __________ to His voice.

Verse 31 states that our God is a compassionate God.

What will He remember? ____

Verse 36 shows the compassion of God by reminding the Israelites of God's discipline. That discipline was to lead the Israelites to know the truth of verse 39. Write that truth here: ____

____

Read Deuteronomy 4:40.

What is the provision of verse 40? ____

____

What condition must be met in order to gain these things?

____

Now turn to chapter 6 of Deuteronomy. This chapter is titled in my Bible as "Obey God and Prosper". Read this entire chapter, but let's focus on verses 4-7, 13, and 18. Verses 4-5 are part of the Jewish Shema. These are verses found in Deuteronomy and Numbers that are repeated several times a day by the Jewish leaders and faithful Jews as part of their liturgy.

Why do you think they chose these two verses as a part of such an important tradition?

____

____

What do these two verses mean to you?

____

____

____

Verse 6 and 7 tells us how important these verses are to God. He wants them not just written down or read daily, but to be imprinted upon our hearts – to be memorized, thought about, and acted upon. And then, they are to be taught to our children diligently. The Jewish nation didn't understand this at this time. They religiously followed verses 8-9 and wore boxes (called phylacteries) on their foreheads with these verses tucked inside and set them into boxes by their doors and touched them when entering and exiting, but they didn't put them into the deep recesses of their hearts. It's kind of like a spelling assignment where you are asked to write each word 20 times. The teacher is not really interested in that sheet of paper that has the words on it; she is using it as a device to get the words into your brain. God was using the boxes as reminders of what needed to be put into their hearts.

Verse 13 further explains God's requirements.

What three things were the Israelites to do? ____________________________________

____

____

If they upheld their end of the covenant, what did God promise? ________________

____

Now turn over to chapter 11. This chapter further tells of the rewards of obedience. Notice that God reminds the Israelites of His discipline in verse 2.

What verses remind you of the Shema?

____

Just a few more passages to go. Turn to Chapter 28:15-68. Here we find the consequences of disobedience.

List the curses that will come because of disobedience. (I found more than 30.)

____

____

____

____

____

____

____

____

____

And, lastly, look at Deuteronomy 30:1-3.

What was the purpose of God's discipline?

____

____

God still disciplines today. It might be through illness, loss, broken relationship with Him, consequences of our actions, lack of direction, and many other disturbing things. But whatever the discipline, it is always from the hand of a loving and compassionate God who desires above all else that we might turn back to Him and love Him with all of our heart, soul, and might.

Through it all we see God's grace (Deuteronomy 30:1-3). Remember the rules that God laid down for His people when at Mt. Sinai? We learned in lesson 5 that God's rules are a hedge about us to keep us from harm. But God gave us free will. If we choose to step outside of God's hedge of protection by doing something sinful, having an attitude of rebellion, or refusing to confess and repent, He will discipline us to bring us back into fellowship with Himself.

God, as our Father, delights in us. – so says Proverbs 3 verse 12. Our response to God should be obedience, love, respect, and a desire to be with Him and to please Him. That's where wisdom comes in (again). Verses 13 – 20 remind us of wisdom and her rewards. Finding how to please God and how to respond to God is all wrapped up in understanding who God is – His attributes, His character, His desires, and His heartbeat.

We should seek for this wisdom (found within Scripture and through prayer) diligently. It should be utmost in our minds. "For what is a man profited, if he shall gain the whole world, and lose his soul?" (Matthew 16:26). Wisdom's gain is better than jewels, gold, or silver. She is life itself. Verses 19-20 remind us again of the inability to separate Jesus and wisdom. Wisdom was the very power of creation, as Jesus formed the universe. That same wisdom will be our provision, protection, and even our confidence.

Add verses Proverbs 3:11-20 to your charts. (Appendices A and B)

Keep working on memorizing the verses for Proverbs 3. We will start on verses 5–8 tomorrow.

Seeking a Savior

Lesson 14

Read Proverbs 3: 13-26.

According to verse 14, whose profit is better than silver and gain is better than fine gold? ____

Do you think that the majority of people in today's world would agree with this statement? Why or why not? ________________________________

____

Upon reading verse 15, you might disagree, thinking that there are things in this world that you desire more than God's wisdom: popularity, friends, a better body, to be smarter in school, an opportunity to attend college, different skills, etc.

What are your desires?

____

____

Right now all those things seem most important, but the truth is that when you gain God's wisdom it will include the right priority for all those things. God may choose to bless you with your desires, or He may not. But when you have stood before God in prayer and trusted Him and known the joy that comes from being in His presence, all these things will not seem so important. When you truly grasp the reality that you are a child of the King, an heir to heaven, and can sit upon His lap and talk to God, then you will have gained wisdom and all the treasures of earth will dim in comparison.

The 7 byproducts of seeking God are listed in verse 16-18.

List them below:

1.
2.
3.
4.
5.
6.
7.

Verses 19 and 20 remind us why Christ is to be our unmovable foundation. He is timeless, eternal. His wisdom is from before time and will be after time. Upon it alone can we stand no matter our culture, our nation, our era.

Where do we find this wisdom? God's Word, first of all. The Bible is inexhaustible, therefore this study, as well as any Bible study, is just a guide. God's depth cannot be reached, but it is okay to dive down deep again and again to gain more of his treasures. Don't read the Bible through and then stick it on the shelf as another book accomplished.

"For the word of God is quick, and powerful, and sharper than any two-edged sword." (Hebrews 4:12)

Read it, memorize it, think about, pray through it, and read it again.

Read 2 Timothy 3:16. What four actions is Scripture profitable for?
1.
2.
3.
4.

Proverbs 3:21-26 gives us some benefits from choosing wisdom. Put them on your wisdom chart in Appendix B. (I found 10.)

Another source of God's wisdom is reading biographies of men and women of faith through the ages. As you see God interact and respond to their prayers and faithfulness, your own faith will soar. As you see men and women humble themselves and walk according to God's Word, you will see them triumph over great odds. They were not always the richest, the prettiest, the most popular, etc., but they were at peace, used by God and looking forward to an eternity with God. Missionary stories, stories of martyrs of the faith, and great leaders in ministry can round out your literary heritage. Joni Erickson-Tada, Corrie Ten Boom, Watchman Nee, George Fuller, Bruchko, and Brother Andrew are among my favorite giants of the faith.

These men and women chose the narrow gate of Matthew 7:13-14.

"Enter ye in at the strait gate: for wide is the gate, and broad is the way, that leadeth to destruction, and many there be which go in thereat: Because strait is the gate, and narrow is the way, which leadeth unto life, and few there be that find it."

That gate is the wisdom and truth of the Scriptures. You can bet your life on them. I would emphasize here, again, that salvation is not through works. When Jesus said, "It is finished," He, and He alone accomplished our salvation. However, that salvation and love for our Savior will lead us to walk in a way that pleases God. God actually changes our hearts and desires to make us want to live our lives in a God-pleasing way. (Psalm 37:4 and 2 Corinthians 5:17). He transforms our purposes, goals, expectations, and our very essence when we renew our minds daily by abiding in Christ Jesus. (Romans 12:2). These verses in Proverbs then are a gift from God as they tell us how to live in order to please God. Our own hearts give testimony to these words as we study them, live them, and reap the benefits and blessings of our God. The way, however, is narrow. Many of these life principles are not popular in today's culture. To live them out may require us to buck society, to say no to pleasure, pride, luxuries, and friends. In the end, God promises us eternal life and for now, peace, a relationship with God, and His guidance – a life and walk of faith. It's hard. It's lonely sometimes. But, it's worth it.

> Turn to your Wisdom chart and put in verses 13-26. Don't forget to color code these verses yellow for wisdom.

Turn to Appendix C and draw pictures for Proverbs 3: 5-8. Begin memorizing this section of Scripture now.

Doing Desirable Deeds

Lesson 15

Read Proverbs 3:27-30.

Today we begin what I call the practical advice section of Proverbs. What a deep well of suggestions for putting our faith to work in our day to day lives.

Let's start with verse 27.

> "Withhold not good from them to whom it is due, when it is in the power of ________________ ________________ to do it."

This flows from the love of Christ in us. If we are grounded in His Word and abiding in Him moment by moment, the fruit of the Spirit (Galatians 5:22) will flow freely in our lives. Thus the fruits of love, kindness, and goodness will flow to others when it is in our power to do it.

I have never seen a tree struggling and laboring to push fruit out of its limbs. Rather, a tree puts its roots deep into the ground and takes in water and nutrition and the fruit is a natural by-product. In the same way, we are to be rooted in the Word of God and drinking the Living Water and "eating" the Word daily. Naturally from out of our being will grow the fruits as evidence of our faith and trust. Begin looking for opportunities to bless others. A good deed done in secret without expecting any return blesses the recipient as well as the giver.

My husband managed an apartment complex while in college. We were not yet married, but I learned from him his desire to replant a flowerbed at the apartments the next day. A girlfriend and I snuck up to the apartments at midnight and planted that garden for him. Imagine his surprise the next morning when he stepped outside ready for a couple of hours of work and was greeted with bright, colorful marigolds and cheerful daffodils.

Choose two people that you can do something special for just because it is in your power to do it.

Person 1: Who?
What?

Person 2: Who?
What?

Now look at verse 28. This verse follows in the vein of verse 27. A look at Deuteronomy 24:15 will help to clarify this verse. If someone is withholding what rightly belongs to another, he is harming the other and causing doubt and anxiety. This can become a source of power that people misuse. They feel that by having another's possessions, they can manipulate and rule to their advantage. This is not a God honoring attitude. If we finish each

day's business with others by the end of each day, both parties are free to move on. And we are free to go before the Lord with a clear conscience and wait upon His bidding. Now let's finish up with verses 29 and 30. Abiding by what we learned in verse 27, we naturally avoid devising harm or contending with a neighbor without cause.

> 1 Thessalonians 4:11 tells us, "And that ye study to be_______________, and to do your ___________business, and to work with your ______________hands, as we commanded you."

There is a right time to contend or confront another, but not without cause.

> Add these verses to your wisdom chart. (Proverbs 3:27-30)

Keep working on your memorization of Proverbs 3:1-8. We put actions to the words to help us remember them better. Give this a try.

Choices and Consequences

Lesson 16

You will begin to notice that much of Proverbs is written in two line sayings. These sayings are called couplets. There are three basic types of couplets that you will encounter throughout the book of Proverbs. The first kind is the most used – opposites. These couplets state a principle in the first line and give an opposite statement in the second, but the two lines never contradict each other. Some examples of this type of couplet are Proverbs 3:22, 3:33-35.

3:35: "The wise shall inherit glory: but shame shall be the promotion of fools."

Two different attitudes – wise and foolish. Two different outcomes – honor and dishonor. This type of couplet always leaves the reader with a very clear cut choice. Do I want honor or dishonor? Then do I need to act wisely or foolishly? Let's look at verses 3:31-35 today and tomorrow. We'll learn about the other two types of couplets in later lessons.
Fill out the following chart:

	ATTITUDE	OUTCOME	ATTITUDE	OUTCOME
vs. 32	froward	abomination	upright	God's secret (intimacy with God)
vs. 33				
vs. 34				
vs. 35				

Go ahead and read these verses and add them to your foolish and wise charts (Appendixes A and B).

Proverbs 3:31 "Envy thou not the oppressor,
And choose none of his ways."

At first glance we might say, "Why would I envy an oppressor or violent man in the first place?" Many envy the adventure, excitement and riches of such a lifestyle. Not all, but some men of violence seem to have it all – the house, the cars, the fame, the fun. It's the popular boys and girls who have all the friends and seem to break all the rules.

Read Psalm 10.

This is a description of how we see reality, but remember God is bigger and sees the whole picture all the way to the end and His judgments will stand forever.

Now flip back a Psalm and look at Psalm 9:7-10.

Will the riches of the wicked stand forever? No. What will stand forever?

____

In verse 8, the Word proclaims that God's judgment will be done in righteousness and in ______________________.

Verse 10 is a promise that you can stand on.
Write it out below.

____
____
____
____

Proverbs 3:32 "For the froward is abomination to the Lord:
but his secret is with the righteous."

In this verse we are introduced to the "forward (or crooked) man" – the man whose ways are not right and straight forward before the Lord. This man is an affront, an abomination before the very God who created him. Abomination is a very strong word. It is not something that merely disgusts but something that utterly repulses. A crooked man utterly repulses God. The creature that God made to love and draw to Himself has become an abomination to its very Creator. Many would say, "Oh, I'll get things right with God later." But later may never come and that one would die utterly repulsive to God to be put away from Him for eternity. Even if such a one does turn to God later, it will be with many regrets. For even though God's mercy is greatest, man must live with the consequences of his actions. One of those consequences is often a hardened heart – a heart which would not hear God and obey.

But, the opposite is also true. His secret is with the righteous: God is intimate with the upright. As believers we have access to the very throne of God. He knows our heartbeat and we know the very mind of Christ. (1 Corinthians 2:16). He desires an intimate relationship with us. When we are walking uprightly, we too, as His children, desire that intimacy with God. But oh. How we run and hide when we know we have sinned – just as Adam did in Genesis 3:9-10. That intimate relationship can be restored once again by confession as read in I John 1:9.

Write this verse out here:

____
____

Wow! To be intimately known by God. You can know that you are moving toward God when your desire is not for God's benefits but, rather, for God Himself.

Do you desire His blessing, protection, provision, mercy, and love, or do you desire Him? ______________________

Pray a prayer of praise to God for He knows and loves you.

Proverbs 3:33 "The curse of the Lord is in the house of the wicked:
but he blesseth the habitation of the just."

Let's begin by talking about a curse. God is the same yesterday, today, and forever. (Hebrews 13:8) Although God, as revealed in the New Testament, is a God of love and mercy, He is still a God of justice as revealed in the Old Testament. Even in the Old Testament, God shows great mercy and faithfulness and has such a desire to bless His children. However, He is a holy God who cannot stand before sin. Therefore, God curses sin and the sinner, not out of perverse anger, but out of a heart of tough love. If it takes a curse to turn some towards God, then God will oblige. The curse is used as a hedge to give man direction and consequence. A study of Deuteronomy is very eye-opening to understanding God's heart within the scope of His curses and blessings.

Take a moment and glean over Deuteronomy chapters 6-8 and 28 and 29:15-20.

It is all summed up in Deuteronomy 29:15-20. God wants to bless. But since He gave us a free will to choose, He sets out for us the option of His curses (if we so choose) in order that we might turn back to Him.

This is an important principle to remember some day when you have children. They will be wonderful, of course, but they will disobey. You can take it as a personal affront and get angry or you can set up a system of blessings and curses (disciplinary actions). The best way to discipline as a parent is to be like a police officer, emotionally undetached, but meting out prearranged consequences. In our home we set up a poster with lists of actions and consequences. We found the best incentives to be poker chips. Each child had his own color. We went out and bought a "store" – several desirable items of various cost and we put price tags on them to be redeemed by poker chips.

One Mom that I shared this with took her daughter clothes shopping and then came home, hung them all in a closet and tagged them. Her daughter then had to earn them back. We have included getting to have a date with Mom or Dad, getting to have a friend over, as well as toys, roller blades, etc. It is a great way for the children to learn about immediate gratification or saving for the big prize. Each child made a "token" bucket and we set the rules down in writing. Some of our rules included doing chores with a smile and good attitude, remembering our manners, or doing extra nice things for a sibling. All of these actions deserved tokens. On the other hand, tokens could be taken away for hitting, yelling, disrespect, etc. The key to the system is to be consistent and to have prearranged consequences. You can always add some as they crop up.

Spankings were saved for dishonesty and rebellion. We also included push-ups, weeding, etc.

Also notice in this verse, what is cursed or blessed – the house, the dwelling place. Our decisions, choices, and actions affect not only ourselves, but all of those within our family.

Practical Proverbs 

This is true of not only the husband and wife, but also the children. Each of us has an option of being a curse or a blessing; and it all depends on our choices to be wicked or upright before the Lord.

See Proverbs 10:1. This is a great verse to memorize.

Are you are blessing or a curse in your home? ____________________________

We all are both sometimes.

List a time when you were a blessing:

____

List a time when you were a curse:

____

You have the option, the choice to make daily, hourly, minute by minute.

Getting What You Give

Lesson 17

Proverbs 3:34 "Surely He scorneth the scorners:
but he giveth grace unto the lowly."

A scorner is equivalent to a proud man – one who thinks he knows everything and yet understands so little. A scorner is the man who shakes his fist at God and says, "I can live my own life; I don't need You." He scorns God's wisdom to give good gifts and instead tries to horde up earth's treasures. He laughs at loving his enemies; rather, he seeks revenge. God will shake His head at such a one.

But. *But*, the Word says, "God gives grace unto the lowly." What is grace? It is best described along with God's mercy. Mercy is not getting what we deserved (death, separation from God), whereas grace is getting what we don't deserve (God's love, intimacy, forgiveness). It often takes circumstances beyond our control, a disaster, a personal battle, a physical, emotional, relational breakdown before we stand before God and say, "I can't do it on my own, I need God." And God's grace is then poured down upon His child.

Paul, the great apostle of the New Testament cried out to God in his affliction three times (2 Corinthians 12:7-10). God's response was not taking the affliction out of Paul's life, but rather, He replied, "My grace is sufficient for thee." God wanted Paul to keep the affliction and lean on God rather than for God to heal him and for Paul to lean on himself. Yes, God can and does heal. But He is a sovereign God who knows what's best for each of us and sometimes we need His grace more than we need to be delivered from our affliction. God's grace brings peace in the midst of the storm, the comfort of His presence, full knowledge of His forgiveness. It also acts as a balm or salve to soothe the emotions of our afflictions.

What do your afflictions bring? – grace or prideful independence?

____

Try leaning on God and being bathed by His grace.

Proverbs 3:35 "The wise shall inherit glory:
But shame shall be the promotion of fools."

Glory: Respect and distinction, great privilege, esteem; to be thought well of and to have a good reputation; to gain favor with God and man. (Luke 2:52)

Wow! Sounds great. How do we get it? By being wise.

Write the definition of wisdom from lesson 1: ______________________

____

Practical Proverbs 

Simply put: Live God's way and gain honor. Live your way and receive dishonor.

How do we know God's way? It's all written down for us in God's Instruction Book – the Bible. We are to "on it meditate day and night." (Psalm 1:2)

Are you having daily time reading God's Word? ___________

We can know God's way through prayer. You and your best friend enjoy spending time together. You learn about each other that way. You talk and you listen. We learn God's way the same way. We talk to Him and we listen.

Do you spend daily time in prayer speaking and listening? ______________

A third way to know God's way is to read about good and bad examples from history. We've already talked about some of the good ones, but here a few rotten apples that we can learn from as well: Hitler, Stalin, Machiavelli, Howard Hughes, the Shah of Iran, etc.

Think of someone you honor and list ten characteristics of that person.
Person: ________________________

1.	6.
2.	7.
3.	8.
4.	9.
5.	10.

Think of someone you dishonor (or think badly of) and list 10 characteristics of that person.
Person: ________________________

1.	6.
2.	7.
3.	8.
4.	9.
5.	10.

Which person shows wise characteristics? _________________________

Which person displays foolish character traits? ______________________

Add these two verses to your charts. (Proverbs 3:34-35)

Review Proverbs 3:1-8 and be ready to say them aloud tomorrow.

Wisdom – Perfect Prize

Lesson 18

Chapter 4 of Proverbs is again a treatise on wisdom. We will look at verses 1-13 today.

According to verse 5, what should we seek to own?

____

Vs. 6 What will wisdom do if we don't forsake her, but, rather, love her?

____

Vs. 7 What is the beginning of wisdom? ______________________________

Will wisdom by itself be enough? __________________________________

What else will you need? ____

Vs. 8 If I prize wisdom what will I get? ______________________

Vs. 8-9 If I embrace her what will I get? ______________________

Vs. 10 says that if the son accepts these teachings from his father, it will gain him what? ____

Vs. 13 How is wisdom gained? ______________________________________

Okay. It sounds great but now we need to make it practical. Review your memorized definition of wisdom. We also see wisdom personified in a perfect form in Christ Jesus (see lesson 12).

So, before we can gain wisdom (your memorized definition), we must get wisdom (Jesus Christ).

Can an unbeliever be wise? __________

When we recognize Jesus as the Son of God and repent of our sins and decide to let Him be the Lord of our lives, then we have begun our journey for wisdom. Matthew 6:33 reemphasizes this concept: "But seek ye first the kingdom of God and his righteousness; and all these things shall be added unto you."

What must we acquire first? Jesus. Then all the cares of the world will fall into place. (Matthew 6:25-32).

Philippians 4:6 reminds us to "Be careful for nothing, but in everything by prayer and supplication with thanksgiving let your requests be made known unto God. And the peace of

God, which passeth all understanding, shall keep your hearts and minds through Christ Jesus."

Wow. Jesus will keep (guard) our hearts and minds. Proverbs 4:6 promises us that wisdom will keep (guard) us. What a mighty God we serve. If we do as Proverbs 3:6 says, "…In all thy ways acknowledge him, he shall direct thy paths straight." Put Jesus first (quiet times, obedience, prayer, good decisions based on God's Word, and the leading of the Holy Spirit), then He will take care of the rest. He will exalt you, give you peace, honor you, give you long days, keep you from stumbling, and give you life. Does it sound like a journey you want to take? If Christ Jesus is your Savior and Lord, then hold on – keep on studying the Word and continue to grow daily in Him.

Does all of this mean that Christians will never have bad things happen to them? Does it mean that Christians will never be discouraged or sick? What about Romans 8:28? Turn to that verse now and read it. Notice that it says that God will work all things to our good, not that all things will be good. Christians get sick, die, get abused, and suffer depression. Jesus reminded us that in this world we will face persecution and have troubles. (Matthew 5:10, John 15:20). But Jesus also reminds us that He will be with us always. (Hebrews 13:5) He gives us strength and joy in the midst of this earth's sorrows.

Don't forget to add these verses to your wisdom chart. (Proverbs 4:1-3)

Start working on your memorization of Proverbs 3:9-10.

Superb Scriptures

Lesson 19

Let's break away from Proverbs and get a taste of the longest chapter in the Bible – Psalm 119. Yesterday we learned that wisdom comes from instruction. That instruction is found in God's Word. The understanding we need comes through the Holy Spirit as we study God's Word.

Look up 1 Corinthian 2:12-13 and fill in the blanks.

> "Now we have received, not the spirit of the __________________, but the Spirit which is of _____________ , that we might know the things that are ___________ given to us of God. Which things also we speak not in the words which __________ wisdom teacheth, but which the _____________ ____________ teacheth; comparing spiritual things with spiritual."

> Who is our teacher? ______________________________

Without Jesus and the Holy Spirit, we can't understand, but because we have Jesus and the Spirit, we can learn the things of God. Ask Him to open your eyes of understanding and explain the Scriptures to you.

In the original Hebrew language Psalm 119 was done as an acrostic with each line beginning with a different Hebrew letter. Peruse chapter 119 and see if you can find words or phrases that define or explain God's Word to complete this acrostic.

B

I

B

L

E

G

O

D

'S

H

O

L

Y

W

O

R

D

The psalmist had a lot to say about God's Word and its importance in our lives. He used 176 verses to tell us about it.

Working Out a World View

Lesson 20

In contrast to Proverbs 4:1-13 where wisdom showed us her graces, verses 14-17 and verse 19 give us the picture of one who refuses this wisdom. First of all, recognize that going wisdom's way or the wicked way is a choice. Yes, our circumstances influence us, but we must each take responsibility for our choices that lead day by day to the make-up of our lives.

Proverbs 4:14 says, "Enter not into the path of the wicked
And go not in the way of evil men."

It sounds like a volitional choice. You can choose, therefore *Go not.*

This verse is an introduction to the second type of couplet found in Proverbs. It is a restatement. A line of instruction is given and to emphasize its importance, it is restated in the second line with different wording. In Biblical writings, the more something is repeated, the more important it is. The Biblical writers did not have suffixes *-er* or *-est* to add to a word to show its comparative and superlative forms so words are repeated for emphasis.

What word is repeated in Isaiah 6:3? ____________________

Revelation 19:16? __________________________________

Here in Proverbs 4:14, the writer wants to get our attention. Hey. This is important.

Verse 15 is another restatement and gives further direction to verse 14:

"Avoid it; pass not by it;
Turn from it, and pass away."

Notice in verse 14 that wicked is preceded by an article "the" making it a noun. This is not just speaking of an evil deed done here or there but following after wicked men and their ways. We will all stumble and fall occasionally, but God's provision is 1 John 1:9 – confession and forgiveness. (Don't forget: as God forgives you, forgive yourself also and do Philippians 3:13-14).

Write what Philippians 3:13-14 tells you to do. ____________________________
____
____

Proverbs 4:16-17 continues by telling us the consequences of a wicked life.

Be sure to add these to your foolishness charts in Appendix A.

Practical Proverbs

It is interesting to note that the wicked are not entirely without sleep, apparently, after they have committed evil, they do sleep. Wickedness becomes like a drug or an intoxicating drink; they must continue to do wickedness in order to gain a few moments of sleep. (see Proverbs 4:17)

Proverbs 4:19 (we'll discuss verse 18 tomorrow), tells us about the confusion, chaos, hopelessness and blindness of the wicked. They are so blind to wisdom, understanding, instruction, and spiritual insight that they do not even know why they stumble. If you've ever tried to reason with a non-Christian who is far from God's calling, you will understand this. It is impossible to begin on the same page and so you will never agree on the final outcome.

Notice that the warning in verse 14 does not say not to earnestly go seeking evil, or do not engross yourself in evil, but merely, "Enter not into the path…" and "Go not in the way…". Just stepping into a rampaging river can lead to your physical destruction; so it is spiritually: just stepping into that path – one drink, one drug, one lie, one cigarette – and you can be swept away into wickedness as a habit and a lifestyle. The best rule here is "Flee temptation," and never "try it out" to begin with.

This is a great time to study "World Views". A world view is just a person's body of beliefs. A world view answers 8 questions. Write a brief answer to the following questions to summarize your world view.

1. Who are we?

2. Where did we come from?

3. What does it mean to be human?

4. Why am I here?

5. What is wrong?

6. What is the solution? Is there a God?

7. Where are we going?

8. How can we get there?

Your answers to these questions define you as a Christian, a communist, a naturalist, an existentialist, etc. A great book to get you started in a world view study is *The Universe Next Door* by James W. Sire. Check out *C.S. Lewis' Mere Christianity* and all of Francis Schaeffer's and Chuck Colson's books. *Mind Siege* by Tim LaHaye and various titles by David Noebel are also very good. There are also several good websites about worldviews. Check out http://www.projectworldview.org/questions.html and http://www.worldview.org/.

It's time to add two more verses to your memorization. Draw pictures for verses 11 and 12 in appendix C.

Heart Health

Lesson 21

Proverbs 4:18 is such a contrast to where we left the evil person in yesterday's lesson. It is also our introduction to the third type of couplet – the enhancement. Line one will give its information and line two will follow by adding further information to it. These are often difficult to differentiate from the restatements; the clue is to look for additional information. In verse 18 line one reads, "But the path of the just is as the shining light." Line two adds, "that shineth more and more unto the perfect day."

What a difference from the darkness and hopelessness of Proverbs 4:17. The just sees his way and walks securely in it in front of all who might see, and has always an upward hope that his way will be "more and more" (more clearly guided and seen) all the way until the perfect day (heaven).

Now we begin to see clearly why this father (Solomon) writes with such earnestness to his son – not to put him down, or keep him from having fun, but rather that he might taste the glorious light, rather than to stumble along in the dark. Read Proverbs 4:20-22 and add life and health to your wisdom chart in Appendix B.

To lead such a life is not easy and requires constant guarding. Read Proverbs 4:23:

> "Keep (guard) thy heart with all diligence; for out of it are the issues of life."
>
> Write out 2 Corinthians 10:5 ______________________________________
> ____
> ____
> ____
> ____
> ____

Practice asking yourself a few questions about each thought or plan that comes into your mind until they become habit.

1. Is this pleasing unto the Lord?
2. Is this my thought?

Satan often puts thoughts into our minds, and being such a crafty fellow, he will put them in first person. For example, "I'm no good", "I'm just stupid", "I'm ugly". It is best to combat these with Scripture: "I am fearfully and wonderfully made", and "all our works will be tested by fire."

For further discussion on renewing your mind read Annabelle Gilliam's book for girls: *The Confident Woman*. For guys, her husband, Bill's book, *Lifetime Guarantee* is a must.

Proverbs 4:24-27 continue the admonition of this loving parent. Add verse 24 to your foolish chart Appendix A and verses 25-27 to your wisdom chart appendix B. Don't forget to be using your highlighters each day.

Notice again the diligence required in looking straight ahead, watching the path of your feet, and not turning to the right or left but keeping your feet from evil. Being single-focused on God and God's Word will result in a straight path. Singleness of focus in your studies, your work, your relationships, and your career decisions is also extremely important.

"Archbishop Leighton said, 'To him that knoweth not the port to which he is bound, no wind is favorable. He may be well equipped, a good craft, sails set, ballast right, cargo well packed; but he wants somewhere to go, a port to enter. All his activity and preparation are useless without a purpose.'" (Gaining Favor with God and Man, William Thayer, p. 57.)

The Apostle Paul shows singleness of purpose in Philippians 3:13-14. "...but this one thing I do... I press toward the mark for the prize of the high calling of God in Christ Jesus."

If you ask a gymnast where she looks and focuses as she walks the four-inch balance beam, you might expect her to reply, "My feet." but you will be surprised to find that her focus is instead directed to the end of the beam. By watching that sturdy, nonmoving point to which she is headed, her feet find their stable places, one after another. Likewise, if we but put our focus on Christ and direct our attention only to His desires and plans – we will be established – solid and permanent.

To neither turn to the right or left, one must first know the straight path. Where am I going? What activities, relationships, thoughts will get me there? Now, I do not believe that God always shows us His whole plan for our lives, but rather step by step He reveals His greater plan.

Write out Proverbs 16:9 ____

____

____

Write out in the space below where you feel, and prayerfully have considered, is the direction that God is leading you.

Example: to a daily quiet time
to a more respectful attitude toward siblings
to become a more motivated student
to develop my skills with younger children, computers, etc.

Try to list at least 3.

1.	3.	5.
2.	4.	

Work on memorizing and saying Proverbs 3:1-12. Act it out if you need to.

Scintillating Sin

Lesson 22

Chapter 5 of Proverbs begins again with a plea: "My son, attend unto my wisdom, and bow thine ear to my understanding." It is a lot easier to learn a moral lesson through observation rather than participation. Listen to those who are older, respect their experiences, read books that have good examples of people who have chosen well and prospered, and of people who have chosen poorly and were led to destruction. Many famous artists, philosophers, musicians and politicians were successful in their careers, but because they followed after their own hearts, their lives ended in despair (Van Gogh, Voltaire, Rousseau, Degas, Hemmingway, etc.).

Look at Proverbs 5:3-6. The adulteress is that which leads us from our real Master, Creator. She is sin. In Hebrews we read about Moses who learned the lesson of saying no to sin and yes to eternal life even though sin was enticing.

> Read Hebrews 11:25-26. "Choosing rather to suffer affliction with the people of God, than to enjoy the ________________________ _____ ______________ for a ___________________; esteeming the reproach of Christ greater riches than the treasures of Egypt: for he had respect unto the recompence of the reward."

He was single-focused.

Sin can be fun. It can feel good. It can fulfill for a short time. It is enticing. It offers popularity, acceptance, and friends. It looks good.

> But look at Proverbs 5:4 – "But her end is as bitter as ________________, sharp as a two-edged sword." Verse 5 continues, "Her feet go down to ___________; her steps take hold on hell."

Sin, whether it is pride, disrespect, argumentativeness, bitterness, hate, anger, alcohol, drugs, murder, etc. leads eventually to destruction.

Proverbs 5:9-14 describe what happens to one who continues in sin. Add these to your chart in Appendix A.

Look up Romans 14:11, Philippians 2:10 and Isaiah 45:23-24. When sin entices us, what should we remember? ____

Take today's lesson time to go before God and ask Him to reveal to you any sin in your life. Be still before the Lord. If nothing comes to mind, spend time in praise and adoration for the forgiveness of your sins. If you are convicted of sin, be quick to confess and then remember to praise God for His mercy and grace.

Meditate on Psalm 51:6-13 and Isaiah 1:18.

Contentment or Covetousness

Lesson 23

Read Proverbs 5:15-23. These verses offer a great opportunity to discuss dating or courtship with your parents. Pre-thought out perimeters on physical expression before marriage and the wondrous role of sex within the marriage relationship should be discussed before a young man or woman begins to date. Each family will have their own opinions on this, of course. Our family believes that hand holding while courting is the limit. Save the first kiss for the wedding. A great resource for discussion is Josh Harris' book *I Kissed Dating Goodbye* and its sequel *Boy Meets Girl*. For younger students I recommend Dr. James Dobson's *Preparing for Adolescence* CD or book.

Even though these verses are dealing with faithfulness within marriage, they lead to a greater discussion on contentment. Contentment springs from a grateful heart. When we are satisfied and thankful for what we have, we rejoice in it and are fulfilled. When we begin comparing that which we have to what others have we become unsatisfied and get the wants. This can be coveting someone besides our mate, as in the Proverbs, but it also includes covetousness of clothes, cars, careers, children, relationships, houses, positions, etc.

List things that you tend to covet.

1.
2.
3.
4.
5.

My husband and I have agreed to help each other with this by not looking a catalogs or circulars that come in the mail. We also do not spend our time at the mall or window shopping unless we have something specific in mind. We stick to our grocery list at Wal-Mart and seek permission from one another before impulse buying over $5.00. When we get the wants, we remind each other of all God's blessings, what we do have, and the choices we have made that limit financial income such as homeschooling and being in ministry.

What are some steps that you can take to "flee from temptation"?

1.

2.

3.

4.

5.

List some things that you are grateful to God for:

1.	5.	9.
2.	6.	10.
3.	7.	11.
4.	8.	12.

Lastly, Proverbs 5:21 should help us keep within moral boundaries. "For the ways of man are before the eyes of the Lord, and he (God) pondereth all his paths."

Nothing we do or dwell on is hidden from God and all will be revealed in the end.

Read Psalm 139:1-6.

Verses 1-3 include all of our activity. Verse 4 includes our thoughts. Verse 5 shows Gods omnipresence. These verses should not scare the child of God, but rather comfort him. It's okay if a great and wonderful, loving and forgiving Father knows everything about us – that's safe, because He hides us under His wings and His love is so everlasting. Live within that knowledge and take comfort from the fact that He cares that much for you. Remember that an ounce of prevention is worth a pound of cure. Yes, God's grace extends to those times we mess up, but so much better is it if we obey and stay within His arms of protection.

Add Proverbs 5:22-23 to your foolishness chart in Appendix A.

Be ready to recite Proverbs 3:1-10 tomorrow.

Sneaky Snares

Lesson 24

Read Proverbs 6:1-5. Use another sheet of paper and cartoon these verses.

Here are some explanations that may help.

"If thou be surety for your friend" means "one who makes himself liable for another's debts." – Webster

"If thou hast stricken thy hand with a stranger" means having vouched for someone's character that you really don't know.

Being "snared with the words of thy mouth" and "thou art taken with the words of thy mouth" – this could be a lie, a half-truth (at our house a half-truth is a whole lie.), gossip, outbursts of anger, disputes, foul language, etc.

Read James 3:2-12.

Have you been guilty of sins of the tongue? _______________

Read Proverbs 6:3-5 – Then repent.

This requires humbling yourself to go and confess and to importune, (urge, or entreat persistently) your neighbor. You are not to do this tomorrow, but now before the sun has set. This confession is likened to releasing a gazelle from the hunter's hand or a bird from the hand of the fowler.

Now, a hunter is dangerous to a gazelle, and a fowler is dangerous to a bird thus, surety, pledges, and the words of our mouths can be dangerous to our souls. It is urgent that we be released from such actions. This passage should also reveal to us that pledges and sureties are wrong to begin with. Mom and Dad, don't cosign for a car for your teenager. Let them take on their own responsibilities and face the good or bad consequences of their actions. This leads to further responsibility and the ability to try new things and self-respect.

Add drawings in Appendix C from Proverbs 3:13-14 and start memorizing.

Industrious Industry

Lesson 25

Read Proverbs 6:6-11.

Let's for a moment stop and think about the ant. According to the World Book Encyclopedia, there are more ants than any other insect on earth. They are found all over the world except the extreme North and South poles. Ants are ever busy in the warmer months but hibernate during the winter months, therefore they must collect enough food during the warmer seasons to allow them to hibernate without starving. An ant can carry loads many times heavier than itself, whether they are harvester ants – cutting and collecting seeds; or honey ants – collecting juices from flowers; or "cow-keeping" ants – who keep aphids, leafhoppers and certain caterpillars as pets and collect the honeydew they drop from their abdomens; or slave-making ants who capture another species of ants to do the hard labor; or even army ants who go on hunting expeditions for insects and small animals. Find a drawing of an ant from an encyclopedia or nature book and draw it here.

Ants are constantly on the go and busy. They are industrious. As the author of Proverbs records (Proverbs 6:6), "Go to the ant, thou sluggard; consider her ways, and be wise: which having no guide, overseer, or ruler, provideth her meat in the summer, and gathereth her food in the harvest."

"Idleness" according to William Thayer in his book, Gaining Favor with God and Man, "is the mother of poverty, vice, and crime, having a family too numerous to be counted." When Romans, generals and statesmen, tilled the soil of Italy, the Roman Empire flourished. But when slaves were introduced and labor became discreditable to those who could live without it, the ruling class gave itself to pleasure and luxury; soon corruption was everywhere and the empire fell.

Even Adam was required to labor in the Garden of Eden by His creator – and this before sin entered the world. (Genesis 2:15). Work, or labor, the very ability to accomplish work, is a gift of God. "Idle hands are the devil's workshop," has proven true throughout history. Inner city gangs are a result of such idleness by older teens to younger adults who have not been taught to put their energies towards worthwhile ventures.

Read Proverbs 6:9-11.

What will "Yet a little sleep, a little slumber, a little folding of the hands to sleep" lead to? ____

List the work that God would have you to do.

1. Pray (1 Peter 4:7)
2.
3.
4.
5.

Remember, though, that the work of a Christian is not busyness for the kingdom, but rather prayer first, then obedience. As a student, one of your top priorities in the area of work is school. Make sure you include that one.

Fill in the blanks for Proverbs 3:1-14.

My son, forget not my ______________,
but let thine heart keep my ____________________:
For length of days, and long life,
and ________________, shall they add to you.
Let not _________________ and _________________ forsake thee:
bind them about thine neck;
write them upon the _______________ of thine heart.
So shalt thou find ______________ and good ________________
in the sight of ___________ and ______________.

___________________ in the Lord with all thine heart;
and lean not on you own _________________________,
In all thy ways ______________________ him,
and he shall ___________________ thy _____________.
Be not ___________________ in thine own eyes:
fear the ____________________, and ________________ from evil.
It shall be _________________ to thine navel,
and ____________________ to your bones.
Honour the Lord with thy ___________________,
and with the first-fruits of all thine ____________________:

So shall thy barns be ______________ with ______________,
and thy______________ shall ______________ ________ with new wine.

My son, ____________________ not the chastening of the Lord;
neither be ____________________ of his correction:
For whom the Lord ______________ he correcteth,
even as a father the son in whom he______________________.

____________________ is the man that findeth ____________________,
and the man that getteth _______________________________.
For the ________________________ of it is better than the merchandise of
________________,
and the gain thereof than fine ___________________.

Fooleries of a Fool

Lesson 26

Get your pen and highlighters ready to add to your foolish chart (Appendix A). This is pretty specific. Ready?

Read Proverbs 6:12-19

Verse 12 – Naughtiness, wickedness, and a froward mouth are characteristics of foolishness.

Verse 13 –Winking of the eye, speaking with the feet, and teaching with the fingers are characteristics of foolishness.

Verse 14 – A foolish person devises mischief, has a froward heart, and sows discord.

Verse 15 – the result of all this foolishness is that calamity will come suddenly; instantly he will be broken without remedy.

Verse16 – God hates these things; they are an abomination to Him.

Verse 17-19 – characteristics of a fool:

1. A proud look
2. Lying tongue
3. Hands that shed innocent blood
4. Heart that devises wicked imaginations
5. Feet that be swift in running to mischief
6. A false witness that speaketh lies
7. He that soweth discord among brethren

Ouch. I know we are all guilty of at least one or perhaps two or three of these.

Add them to your chart and let's go back and look at them closer.

The first thing that I noticed is that of these 14 abominations, 5 have to do with our tongue – our words. God says that a wicked man has a froward or perverse mouth. The literal meaning of "perverse" is "Directed away from what is right or good; obstinately persisting in an error or fault." (American Heritage Dictionary).

Notice again that it is a choice. Later on in our studies we will run across Proverbs 18:21: "Death and life are in the power of the tongue, and they that love it shall eat the fruit thereof." Wow. Our words can bring life to a person through praise, truth, teaching, etc. or it can be perverse and bring death. A perverse tongue might include gossip, cursing, cussing, negative criticism, continual belittling, lying, sneering, making fun of, etc. You may be able to add others.

Practical Proverbs

Sowing discord is mentioned twice in this section. First it is a general statement, then a more specific statement – sowing discord among brethren (this includes sisters, too). This is especially loathsome to our God because of the high value God puts upon families. He created families to be a support system, a safe place, a haven from the world. When strife is spread among brothers, there is nowhere where one can be at ease, at rest, comforted. I believe we can also stretch this in New Testament times to the brotherhood of Christians. The world is to know that we are Christians by our love for one another. If we are sowing discord in the family of God, then the church will lose its witness. Our difference lies in the fact that we love one another. That is what will draw the world to investigate Jesus. Don't be part of the problem – watch your tongue. (See Francis Schaeffer's book, *The Mark of a Christian.*)

Let's continue with the tongue's evils. The next one listed is lying. This, of course, includes the out and out falsehood, but I would suggest that it covers much more. At our house, "Half a truth is a whole lie." Boy. That can trip you up. Leading someone to believe something false by your silence – is that not a lie? It really is a question of your heart – if you set out to deceive, it's a lie.

Proverbs 6:13 always brings with it an interesting discussion. Winking of the eye, speaking (signaling) with the feet, and teaching (pointing) with the fingers are all acts of conniving. It is usually done behind your victim's back and usually they are the butt of a joke, unkind remark, or prank. God would rather we not say or do anything that we can't be out front with.

Proud looks is a sin that will catch many a young man or woman. That rolling of your eyes when you don't agree or think someone doesn't know what they are talking about is nothing but pride. It's a good thing to catch it now and practice not rolling your eyes, but rather throw up a prayer of thankfulness for the one in your life that sometimes frustrates you.

"Hands that shed innocent blood" includes, but is not limited to, abortion, infanticide, and euthanasia.

And it all comes from the heart. A heart that devises wicked plans or devises evil will manifest itself through the words and actions of the fool.

> Write out 2 Corinthians 10:5.
>
> ____
> ____
> ____
> ____

As you become "transformed by the renewing of your mind," (Romans 12:2), your words and actions will come under the command of the Holy Spirit and will be transformed as well.

> Put a star by any of the following foolish actions that you sometimes get caught doing. Begin to pray now that God will help you "catch" yourself the next time you do this and choose to repent and give a blessing instead.

gossip	cursing	cussing	criticism	belittling	lying
sneering	making fun	sowing discord	proud looks		
speaking with the feet		teaching with the fingers (literally or in your mind)			

Be ready to recite Proverbs 3:1-14 tomorrow.

Directing Discipline

Lesson 27

Read Proverbs 6:20-28.

Let's focus today on discipline – God's discipline. Your memory work of Proverbs 3 includes these lines: "My son, despiseth not the chastening of the Lord; neither be weary of his correction: For whom the Lord loveth he correcteth; even as a father the son in whom he delighteth."

The only commandment with a promise is "Honour thy father and thy mother, as the Lord thy God hath commanded thee; that thy days may be prolonged, and that it may go well with thee, in the land which the Lord thy God giveth thee." (Deuteronomy 5:16)

Proverbs 6:20 is a practical step in that honoring. Time to check your heart.

When your father or mother disciplines you, do you harbor resentment, wallow in bitterness, or are you quick to repent and quick to reconcile? ___________________________

____

Remember discipline does not just refer to punishment, but also includes teaching of those habits which will lead one to a full and healthy life. For example: How many times have you been told to brush your teeth directly after eating? When you have disciplined yourself to do this without parental reminders, you are well on your way to maturity. My husband often comforts me after a long day of reminders to our five boys saying, "God gave them to us for 18-20 years because He knew we would have to say the same things every day for that whole time for them to finally get it." It's not nagging – it's training.

2 Timothy 3:16 reminds us that the Bible is the instruction manual for life and is perfect for what four things?

1.
2.
3.
4.

One more word on the benefits of discipline:

Let's look at 2 Timothy 2:3-6. What three careers are our Christian walk compared to?

1.
2.
3.

We are soldiers of Christ and need to be about disciplining ourselves to the rigors of military life. We are in a race and need to be disciplined so that we might run to win, and, as a farmer, who has been disciplined in his labors and will reap the benefits of his hard work, so we, too, who labor diligently will reap eternal life with Christ Jesus our Lord.

Those who have been reared by discipline learn to respect and be grateful for the rules, boundaries, and confines. On the other hand, if one has not bent their knee to discipline's molding power, he finds himself fighting discipline as if it were the enemy – taking away his rights of freedom, of choice, and freedom of speech, eventually loathing any and all authority placed over him including the loving, caring, faithful Creator God.

At that point, Proverbs 6:24-28 becomes reality. These verses compare the consequences of not being disciplined to giving in to the evil woman. She personifies pride, selfishness, and all the sins that come from a heart that is dripping with evil.

Write verse 27 here:

____
____
____

What is your answer to this question? _____________________________

Can a man ignore discipline and not suffer the bad consequences? ____________

Draw pictures in Appendix C for Proverbs 3:15-16. Make up actions for these verses.

Leading Lust

Lesson 28

Discipline, we learned yesterday, is a safeguard. If we succumb to Biblical, Godly discipline, we also reap the benefits of Godly living. Proverbs 6:24-28 tells us what the result is of denying or turning away from that discipline. Remember in the Old Testament, adultery is often the imagery used for all things that pull us away from God (including but not limited to a sexual affair.)

In Proverbs 6:25 where does the lie begin? ___________________________
(Quick note – even though Proverbs seems to be talking to men only, don't forget, sisters, that we too can fall into the same traps and troubles, for we are a part of mankind.)

Sin begins in your heart. Your heart is the doorway of choice. Even Jesus was tempted. It is not sinful to be tempted or to have a tempting thought. What we do with that temptation or thought leads us to sin or righteousness. James 1:14-15 holds the key.

Write these verses out here. ____
____
____
____

This is the LSD principle. Lust leads to sin, which leads to death.
L – lust
S – sin
D – death

But where is the beginning of lust? Lust is the deep desire or longing for something. It can be sexual, but can also be food, acceptance, a bigger house, etc.

Turn to 1 John 2:15-16 and fill in the blanks. "Love not the ______, neither the things that are in the ____________. If any man love the ________________, the love of the Father is not in him. For all that is in the _______________, the lust of the ________, and the lust of the______________, and the ________________ of life, is not of the Father, but is of the ______________________.

We are tempted by what we see, what we desire, what we think will fulfill and bring power.

1 John 2:17 goes on to state that, "And the ________________ passeth away, and the lust thereof; but he that doeth the will of God abideth for ever."

Once again we see choices: the choice between temporary fulfillment and eternal glory with Christ; the choice between the absolute necessity of hiding God's Word in our hearts to keep from sinning and to be transformed by the renewing of our minds. When you don't make a choice, your default is usually the wrong one.

Many Godly teenagers fall away from Godly principles due to false guilt experienced in these years over sexual desires, urges, thoughts, etc. Please know, dear teenager, that these are a normal part of growing up. Keep them under control, pray, discipline yourself to think on the things mentioned in Philippians 4:8.

According to this verse what should we focus on? Things that are:
1.
2.
3.
4.
5.
6.
7.
8.

Then again, there's always ice cream. When we were questioning one of our boys about how he handles the visual desires when he sees young women scantily dressed, he replied that he thinks about ice cream. It's right, pure, lovely, excellent and worthy of praise. I think God meant to think upon the Words of Scripture, but if ice cream works, go for it. But either way, be quick to forgive yourself, refocus, and most importantly, "Now flee from youthful lusts and pursue righteousness, faith, love and peace, with those who call on the Lord from a pure heart." (2 Timothy 2:22).

If going to the beach and seeing others in swimsuits brings about thoughts of sex then don't go to the beach. If the internet poses enticing views, stay offline or get a filter. But know that you are normal and by disciplining yourself now, you will find so much more pleasure, ease, and joy in your life partner's arms later on.

If you succumb to even dwell on such thoughts they will lead to sin (even sinful attitudes) as Proverbs 6:26-28 state they, "Will reduce you to a loaf of bread", "burn you", and "scorch you".

Color and add verses 6:21-35 to your foolish chart (Appendix A).

Fill in the blanks for Proverbs 3:13-16:

Happy is the man that ______________ wisdom,
and the man that ______________ understanding.
For the ____________________ of it is better than the _____________ of silver,
and the gain thereof than ______________ gold.
She is more __________________ than _______________:
And all the things thou canst ______________are not to be compared unto her.
Length of__________ is in her ________________ hand;
And in her _______________ hand _________________ and ______________.

New Nature

Lesson 29

Read all of Proverbs chapter 7 noting the characteristics (enticements) of sin and the results of sin. Highlight and add to chart Appendix A

1 John has a lot to relate to us about sin. First of all, if someone had never committed a sinful deed or broken a rule (impossible in our flesh or own desires), he would still be a sinner because he inherited that sin nature from Adam. If you ever doubt this inherited sin, just watch a two-year old. No one had to teach him to stomp his foot, or turn away from his mother's voice, or do what he wishes in spite of parental direction. He does have to be trained in righteousness, to learn what *no* means.

In our house, *no* meant, "It's not going to happen so quit asking." Having a three or four-year repeat back the meaning of *no* when he/she wants to throw a fit or argue tends to stop him/her in his/her tracks.

1 John 1:8 says that "If we say we have ________ __________, we deceive ourselves, and the ___________is not in us."

As a Christian, that sin nature is replaced by God's Holy Spirit. We are "a new creature; old things are passed away." (2 Cor. 5:17). The power of the Holy Spirit is upon us to convict us of our sin. However, because we continue to live in a sinful body, in a sinful world, the option is always there to choose to commit acts of sins, even though we've been cleansed from the inherited sin.

Thus 1 John 1:9 says, "If we confess ___________ ____________, He is faithful and just to forgive us of our sins and cleanse us from all unrighteousness."

Even Paul dealt with sin. In Romans 7:14-8:6, he knew and experienced the war we must all face. He knew what was right to do, but failed to do it. Read this passage.

Romans 8:1 is a great verse to memorize. "There is therefore now ______ ____________ for those who are in Christ Jesus." (The KJV adds a condition to this. See note at end of this book.)

This is a good thing. This is a statement of our position in Christ, not about our conduct. We are held accountable for the sinful deeds or attitudes that we have as born again Christians, but sin does not change our position as God's beloved child, redeemed and bought with a forever price. One might ask, "Then, if I am born again, can I go on sinning?" The answer to this is found in Romans 6:1-2. "What shall we say then? Are we to continue in sin so that grace may abound? God forbid. How shall we, that are dead to sin, live any longer therein?"

There are several reasons that as Christians we should leave our sin behind us.

1) Christ died for us. Out of sheer gratitude we should live to please Him.
2) Sins carry with them dire consequences that are not befitting a son or daughter of the King.
3) The laws are put into place for our protection and provision. By following them we will find happiness and great joy.
4) As we strive towards holiness, knowing that we cannot attain it without God, we grow in our relationship with God.
5) Others are watching us. We don't want to give them an excuse not to become a Christian.
6) The fruit of the Holy Spirit cannot grow within us if our roots are not planted deep and arms outstretched to God's goodness.
7) If we are praying and praising God, and desiring to live with Him, the Holy Spirit will convict us of our sin and we will be most miserable.

The key is to live and walk and abide in the Spirit, to be studying the Word of God, memorizing the Word of God, meditating upon the Word, being in a constant state of prayer and communication with our Father in heaven and choosing to put aside the things of this world. That's a big order.

No, we don't have to join a convent or become hermits; there is a balance. A Godly life can be led in America in the 21st century, but it is challenging and requires constant watch, minute by minute choices, and the assurance and hope of Christ. My husband has often said that he felt like a fish swimming upstream as we made unpopular choices such as my staying home to raise the children rather than becoming a career woman; homeschooling; monitoring tv, movies, music, friends, and activities; not allowing our children to stay for extended amounts of time with relatives due to lifestyle differences; and even moving as the Lord opened up to us new avenues of ministry. But it has been worth it all. God has blessed all five boys with hearts ready and wanting to serve Him. They are making wise choices and desiring to live lives worthy of Christ's sacrifice. What more could a parent hope for?

Of course, they are human; they make mistakes, they sin, and they frustrate me with their immaturity at times, but they are quick to repent and striving towards maturity. It is about the relationship. They are my sons. Period. Even when they mess up, I love them. Psalm 37:23-24 sums up God's relationship of love with us. "He delighteth in his way. Though he fall, he shall not be utterly cast down, for the Lord upholdeth him with his hand."

We are God's delight. I imagine a father teaching his son to walk. When that child falls down, Dad is not there with a lecture and a frown or disappointment. No, rather, he picks him up with a giggle and a tickle, sets him back on his feet and lets him try again within the reach of the father's protective embrace.

What nature has God redeemed in you? ________________________________

Does that mean that you will never sin again? ______________________________

When you do mess up, what are you to do? ______________________________

Remember, "There is therefore now no condemnation for those who are in Christ Jesus."

Be quick to repent and strive towards holy living, but know that there is nothing that you can do to lose your position as a child of God.

Draw a picture of a caterpillar.

Where did you draw it – in the sky or on the ground or a leaf? Did you draw it flying? No, a caterpillar can't fly.

Draw a butterfly.

This creature can fly. How sad if we see it walking along the ground trying to find its way.

As born again Christians, we are that butterfly. We can fly and soar above life's circumstances. We have that ability, but how sad it is to see us crawling around, absorbed in the grass of life instead of flying through the skies. This is what happens when we choose, as Christians, to sin. We have the power not to sin, but we don't always use that ability. Make sure that you are living life on an eagle's wing, high above the sin and garbage of this world.

Keep memorizing Proverbs 3:1-16.

Proverbial Puzzle

Lesson 30

Chapter 8 of Proverbs is really a riddle and a very foundational one at that. Here are some of the clues:

8:1 – "Doth not wisdom cry? and understanding put forth her voice?"

8:7 – "For my mouth will speak truth; and wickedness is an abomination to my lips."

8:11 – "For wisdom is better than rubies; and all the things that can be desired are not to be compared to it."

8:17 – "And those who seek me early shall find me."

8:22 – "The Lord possessed me in the beginning of his way, before his works of old."

8:27 – "When he prepared the heavens, I was there…"

8:30 – "Then I was by him, as one brought up with him…"

8:32 – "…for blessed are they that keep my ways."

8:35 – "For whoso findeth me findeth life and shall obtain favour of the Lord."

Still not sure?

Let's narrow it down. Look at:

8:32 – He is the Way
8:7 – He is Truth
8:35 – He is life

Sound familiar?

> Try John 14:6. "___________said to him, 'I am the way, the truth, and the life; no one cometh unto the Father, but by Me.'"

That's right. Jesus is the personification of wisdom. I Corinthians 1:24 states that Christ is the power of God and the wisdom of God. Look at I Corinthians 1:30.

> "But of him are ye in Christ Jesus, who of God is made unto us ___________, and righteousness and sanctification, and redemption."

Jesus was also with God in the beginning. He is worth far more than jewels, by Him kings reign, Power is his, those who seek Him find Him, wealth and righteousness is his, etc.

Practical Proverbs

Find some New Testament verses that answer the Old Testament riddle. You may use a concordance.

Jesus was with God in the beginning ______ John 1:1, 1 John 1:1-3

Righteousness is His. ______________________

Power is His. ______________________

Those who seek Him find Him. ______________________

Wealth is His. ______________________

His mouth will utter truth. ______________________

He wants to endow those who love Him with wealth, to fill their treasuries.

____

Blessed are those who keep His ways. ______________________

Those who hate Him love death. ______________________

Those who find Him find life. ______________________

Be ready to recite Proverbs 3:1-16 tomorrow.

Unfailing Foundation

Lesson 31

We learned yesterday, that Jesus is the personification of wisdom. Wisdom was laid down before time and before creation, in essence, wisdom is the very character of God. Here it is – absolute truth.

Our society is twisting truth to fit each one's circumstances, personality, desires, etc. But, God's Word stands and truth was established from the beginning and exists outside of human experience. Wisdom comes in only one flavor – Truth. And it is absolute truth at that. Truth is honesty, not because your parents tell you so, but because God is honest. Truth is justice because God is just; truth is pure because God is pure; truth is eternal and unchanging because God is eternal and unchanging.

Wisdom, then, is a stable foundation. Jesus is a stable foundation. Truth is a stable foundation. If you build your life, your relationships, your dreams, your desires, your expectations, upon this wisdom, you will stand firm. And, it's not a secret. Wisdom calls out from the heights, from beside the way, at the entrance of doors. So, why are so many blind and deaf to her call?

According to Ephesians 4: 17-19 how did the Gentiles walk? ________________
____
____

They were, "Having the understanding darkened, being alienated from the life of God through the ignorance that is in them, because of the ____________of their __________: who being past feeling have given themselves over unto lasciviousness, to work all uncleanness with greediness."

And in Romans 1:21-25,

People knew God, but did not _____________ Him or give Him ______________.

"Their foolish heart was ____________________. Professing themselves to be wise, they became ______________."

These verses say that they "Changed the truth of God into a lie."

God's mercy and grace is available to all, but one must reach out and accept it. Huxley was a friend of Charles Darwin and one of the biggest proponents of evolutionary biology. He said, "I suppose the reason we leaped at *The Origin of Species* was because the idea of God interfered with our sexual mores." [McDowell, Josh. Evidence That Demands a Verdict (San Bernardino, CA: Here's Life Publishers, 1999).] He could not believe in Christianity although evolution had no proof, because then he would have to change his amoral lifestyle.

Man's unwillingness to submit to God's rules and laws under His redeeming grace keeps them in the dark. They are throwing away the treasure for temporary pleasure. (Hebrews 11:25).

1 Corinthians 2:14 says that "The natural man recieveth not the things of the Spirit of God, for they are foolishness unto him: neither can he know them because they are spiritually discerned." When the Holy Spirit comes to live in our lives, He brings spiritual wisdom and light. We can begin to see things differently; we are made new; our minds are renewed for we have the mind of Christ (1 Corinthians 2:16).

I have been working with a young lady who was raped by her cousin when she was just 14 years old. She later became a Christian and mourned the fact that she was not a virgin. However, in Christ there is now no condemnation (Romans 8:1) and before Him she is now a new creature pure and righteous before Him. She needs to understand this and begin to renew her mind with His promises and accept herself as Christ has declared her – holy and perfect.

Remember, though, renewing our minds is a choice.

Look at Proverbs 8:32-34. According to these verses we must do 7 things. What are these 7 things?

1.
2.
3.
4.
5.
6.
7.

We must hear it and do it. (James 1:22)

Recite Proverbs 3:1-16 out loud.

Wise Words

Lesson 32

Add characteristics and results of wisdom from chapter 8 to your charts. (I found 19).

Find these words in the word search:

Prudence	Discretion	Righteous	Power
Noble things	Hates evil	Knowledge	Justice
Right things	Hates pride	Understanding	Love
Truthful	Sound counsel	Jewels	Riches
Honor	Wealth	Generous	

G P R E G D E L W O N K H I N D V R T L S

N E P O W S P D I S M E O N E W F T L L G

I S N U N D J R I H O J N V E D L T E B N

H O R E N T U L C S W L O R B S D W T H I

S E D I R P S E T A H L R Q R C E U A W H

T M P L M O K I F E C I T S U J Y E H B T

E R E O K O U N D E R S T A N D I N G G E

A I C J L H J S G I R Y B L P G H C T H L

H C N O N W E A L T H C U U R T A N O B B

I H E L P H J S R T D F B P P R T U O D O

W E D E C T R I D I H D I S C R E T I O N

G S U I O U G E S T U H N T F T S S E T N

E M R A G H F C U L Y R L U R U E T C E V

N T P I T O O R P M S E L S H R V A D U H

N L L E P V T H O N O W L T G T I E R O A

O P O M E S O U N D C O U N S E L W I P T

U U S R T R M E D O W P B M C H N U O S E

S R Y R Q T P U N S G N I H T T H G I R S

Illumined Inspiration

Lesson 33

Proverbs 9 continues with wisdom. Notice how stable she seems and how her work is already done. She *has* built her house, *has* hewn out her 7 pillars, *has* prepared her food, *has* mixed her wine, and *has* set her table. She is already established. This reminds me of Ephesians 4:14-15.

Write these verses below:

____

____

____

____

____

We, too, are to be established, grounded, unmovable according to truth, and firm in our beliefs and doctrines. We should test the spirits. (1 John 4:1), take every thought captive, (2 Corinthians 10:5), and be willing and ready to give an account thereof in the day of judgment (Matthew 12:36).

Many believe that the pillars of wisdom were doctrines adopted by the early church. These seven pillars are:

1. Salvation
2. Baptism
3. Doctrine or discipleship
4. Fellowship
5. Breaking of bread
6. Prayer
7. Giving

Notice that wisdom is abundantly supplied to feast and dine all who are willing to seek her out. She never runs out of resources and never has to beg or borrow from others. God's depths are unfathomable. His Word is inexhaustible. You can come to the same verse or passage again and again and Holy Spirit may reveal more depth each time. His Word speaks to my heart, mind, and emotions and meets me where I am, each time either exhorting me, disciplining me, training me, or reminding me of His character, His promises, and His plan.

Read 2 Timothy 3:16-17.

What are the four things that Paul tells Timothy that Scripture is profitable for? I know we are repeating ourselves, so this must be really important.

1.
2.

3.
4.

Another word for *inspiration* is God-breathed. Even though men took up the pen to write the actual words of Scripture onto paper, it was God who first put it upon their hearts and compelled them to write giving them dictation word for word.

2 Timothy 3:17 says that Scripture is adequate, or complete, or capable and will prepare or equip us for every good work. Hebrews 13:20-21 says, "Our Lord Jesus…make you perfect in every good work to do his will." His Word is the training tool that is equipping us to do the will of God, but the Holy Spirit is also involved as we read and study equipping us to do that which pleases God.

How important is it, then, that we study Scripture diligently and deliberately? See 2 Timothy 3:15.

____

____

Write a plan for your personal Bible study below. You can do it book by book or topical – a person of the Bible, characteristics of God, etc. There are also excellent choices at the Christian bookstore or CBD.com. I would suggest you do more than a daily devotional quick read and a verse. You are old enough to begin to digest larger portions of God's Word. Make memorization a part of your plan as well.

My Bible Study Plan

Add pictures to Appendix C from Proverbs 3:17-18.

Comparing Character

Lesson 34

Proverbs chapter 9 is a sandwich with verses 1-6 contrasting verses 13-18. We'll look at these today and the *meat and cheese* verses (7-12) tomorrow.

These two portions of Scripture contrast the wise woman and the foolish woman. Look through these verses and fill out the following chart.

	Wise Woman	Foolish Woman
Character:		
Placement:		
Calls to whom:		
Message:		
Offers:		

As we learned last lesson, the wise woman has a character of preparedness and completion which took diligence and single-mindedness. Compare that to the description of the woman in verse 13. It says she is a woman of folly who is clamorous. The American Heritage Dictionary defines *clamorous* as: 1. violent and turbulent and 2. noisy and unrestrained. Compared to the wise woman, "the foolish woman is clamorous: she is simple, and knoweth nothing." (Proverbs 9:13)

Notice that in verse 3, the wise woman unashamedly calls from the tops of the heights of the city. She is open and does not fear reprisal or an attack on her reputation, whereas the foolish woman of verse 14 "For she sitteth at the door of her house on a seat in the high places of the city." She leaves herself an avenue of escape (back inside), and lingers near the high places, but doesn't venture to call out openly. Her work is best done in private.

This next point is pivotal. Look to whom each woman calls. The wise woman calls out to all who will hear. The foolish calls to those who pass by making their paths straight. Wow. Wisdom is for everyone; foolishness just tries to trap those who are righteous. But the words of their message are the same: "Whosoever is simple, let him turn in hither." (9:4 and 13) The key is the results of their message. To those who follow wisdom and forsake folly is

promised life and the way to understanding. The end result of those who follow folly is stolen water, secret bread, and death.

This lesson will wrap up our wise and foolish charts. Highlight these verses and add them to your charts. Take a look at what you've recorded. The choice is pretty plain, the characteristics clear, and the results eternal.

Practice Proverbs 3:13-18 with actions.

Receiving Reproof

Lesson 35

Here's the *meat and cheese* of our sandwich which has wisdom on one side and foolishness on the other. I see it as a warning, an opportunity for self-evaluation, a chance to repent and turn.

Read Proverbs 9:7-9. Let's evaluate how you receive reproof. Do you listen and heed discipline or do you scoff at your authority figure?

____

Do you turn and tell tales out of anger and resentment about the one who meted out the punishment or do you humble your heart and ask for forgiveness?

____

____

Turn to Hebrews 12:4-13

Who does a father discipline? ______________________

According to Hebrews 12:6, what is God's motive for discipline?

____

If God does not discipline you, according to Hebrews 12:8, what are you?

____

Friend, if you do not know God's discipline, check your heart and be sure that you have bowed at the cross, repented, and have received Christ as Savior and Lord. Then be discerning of the things that go on around you – could it be God's training and disciplining hand?

According to Hebrews 12:9, what should our reaction to the one who disciplines us be? ______________________________________

According to Hebrews 12:10, what is God's motive for disciplining us?

____

Is discipline joyful at the moment? ____________

What does one trained by discipline bear in Hebrews 12:11? ________________

When we encounter discipline we have a choice to make. We can either become stubborn, self-righteous, and vain which leads to rebellion or we can humble our hearts, admit our fault, and let Christ's love heal us and restore us.

What road have you been likely to take?

____

Are you willing to choose wisdom the next time discipline enters your life whether by human authority or God? ____

Back to Proverbs 9: the litmus test is verses 8 and 9.

Do you hate him who disciplines you or do you love him? ____________________

One response is foolish and the other wise. Understanding verse 9 can change the course of your life. Instruction and teaching is for your good; the more you can acquire, the wiser you'll be. This is not the acquisition of just facts, but rather the discerning ability that enables us to use our knowledge to avoid trouble, solve problems, reach goals, and succeed in life – from God's perspective.

Verse 10 should remind us of Proverbs 1:7. It all starts with fearing God. This is the understanding of who God is as Creator, Sustainer, and Savior. Many say this type of fear is really just knowing the awesomeness of God. I disagree; I truly believe that if we saw God we would be terrified. First, because of His holiness; second, because of our sin. We should fear God's disapproval of our sin and yet be able to embrace the love He has for us. We must be able to bow before Him reverently as our King, and also be able to climb into His lap as our Father. Is that not the cross? And that is the beginning.

Proverbs 9:11 is full of God's promise. It should remind you of our memory verses of chapter 3. Wisdom brings not only peace with God and eternal life, but also the number of days and years we will be blessed with here on earth. A holy life is a healthy life.

Proverbs 9:12 is a sober reminder of reality. When all is said and done, it will be you and you alone – stripped of parents, siblings, friends, etc. – that stands before God's throne.

You should now have Proverbs 3:1-26 memorized. Fill in the blanks for Proverbs 3:15-18.

She is more ________________ than rubies:
And all the things thou canst ______________are not to be compared with her.
_____________ ___ _______ is in her right hand;
And in her left hand ______________ and _____________.
Her ways are ways of _________________________,
And all her_________________ are ______________________.
She is a ______________ of _______________ to those who take hold of her:
And ________________ is every one that ____________________ her.

Creating a New Creature

Lesson 36 - 37

We are going to take the next two days to make another chart that will remind you a lot of your wisdom/foolishness chart. This chart will center in the New Testament and will contrast the old nature and the new nature. When we are born again into a relationship with the Father, "…old things are passed away; behold all things have become new." (2 Corinthians 5:17)

Using the following verses fill in the chart on the following pages. Look up each verse and determine the characteristics of the old and new natures. Determine which nature the verse is describing and turn the words into adjectives and record them under the proper heading on the next page. Try filling in the blank: I was ___________ or I am now ______________. For example, in Galatians 5:19 there is a list of the old nature such as immorality, impurity, etc. You would record them as adjectives: "I was immoral"; "I was impure."

You have two days to finish this assignment.

Matthew	5:13-14
John	1:12-13
Romans	1:7
	5:17-18
	6:6-7
	8:1
	8:16-17
	8:37
2 Corinthians	5:17
	5:21
Galatians	5:19-21
	5:22-24
Ephesians	1:7
	2:1-3
	2:4-6
	2:10
	4:17-22
	4:23-32
	6:10
Colossians	2:9-10
	3:5-10
	3:12
Titus	3:3-7
1 Peter	1:16
	1:23
1 John	4:17

OLD NATURE	NEW NATURE

Freedom from Shame

Lesson 38

Now take your chart from yesterday and with a highlighter write the word *shame* in big bold letters right across the words under Old Nature. Cover the whole length of the paper with that ugly word. Shame is the result of being an enemy of Christ. When we are born again, we no longer have to accept the feelings or truth of shame.

According to Psalm 69:19, who knows about our shame?

____

But as children of God, we have a refuge where we never need to be ashamed.

According to Psalm 71:1-3, where is that refuge? ________________________

Explain the following statement: "We are not sinners because we sin, but we sin because we are sinners." ____

____

____

____

Sure, all of us have committed sins. We have lied, or stolen, or been rebellious, or had evil thoughts about someone. Those acts and attitudes and sinful thoughts are a product of our sinful nature. We were born into sin because we were born of Adam, a sinner. I am a Rasmussen, because I was born into the Rasmussen family. I am a sinner because I was born into a sinner's family. However, when I was born again, adopted by God, I became a new creature. I am now born unto righteousness and no longer have to keep sinning. Before I sinned because I was a sinner, now when I sin, it is because I have chosen to. Jesus was not born of Adam; His father was God. Therefore, not only did He never sin, but He never was a sinner.

Would it have done any good to tell the old self to not lie, be peaceable, be forgiving, etc? Why or why not?

____

____

We could fake it for a short time, but without God, we revert back to the old nature. But now that we are in the new nature, we can choose to live according to the Word of God by the power of the Holy Spirit.

How is a victorious Christian life lived? Let me give you three steps.

1. Lay aside the old nature with its practices (Colossians 3:8)
2. Be transformed by the renewing of your mind (Romans 12:2)

3. Put on the new nature (Colossians 3:10 i)n the Greek, each of these is a progressive verb. That means *keep* laying aside the old nature, keep being transformed, keep always putting on the new nature. We are born again one time, but we have to keep being restored – one choice at a time.

There is power in the Word of God – power to renew our minds and to regenerate our lives. Don't leave the Word on a shelf – eat of it daily and be renewed by the Holy Spirit. Then when temptations come, you have the sword (the Word of God) in your hand and ready to be used.

Take your chart and fold the old nature side to the back so that all you can see is the new nature. Across the New Nature list take your highlighter and write *freedom*. In Christ there is freedom to be His child, to grow up in a relationship with Christ. We are no longer bound by the law and the resulting shame.

According to Philippians 3:13-14, what are we to forget?

____

That means the past: past sins that we committed, past sins that were committed against us, *broken promises, broken dreams, unrealistic expectations, and shame.*

According to these verses what are we to reach forward to?

____

That's right: the future. A future with God in control. He is waiting for us at the goal line with a prize.

Release the past, embrace the future. Prayerfully consider what you need to let go of. Write them on a piece of paper and tear it up into tiny pieces and throw it away. Satan no longer has control over you. You are a prince or princess in God's kingdom. Go forward and walk as one.

Sure, Satan will come back and remind you of the past. Remember, "That was then; this is now." The old things are passed away, and all things have become new. Remind him that you threw it all away that now God is your King. On the top of the New Nature list write Prince or *Princess* and your name. Post this list on a mirror or door where you will see it often and remind yourself of all that God has done for you. When those old thoughts or lies come into your mind (Old nature) remind Satan that you are a new creation by reciting some of the characteristics under New Nature. Now would be a good time to take a minute and praise Him for His goodness.

Comparing Characters

Lesson 39

We are going to wrap up the first part of our Proverbs study. I would like you to write a paper contrasting wisdom and foolishness. Use your chart (Appendices A & B) and include both characteristics and results.

Part 2

We are now ready to embark on laying aside of the old nature and putting on the new nature with a practical study through Proverbs concerning various topics that concern you as a teenager and will affect the rest of your life. Remember the writer of Proverbs is good King Solomon. Even though he wasn't perfect, he learned from his mistakes and sought God's wisdom. You can also.

Now look at 1 Corinthians 2:16. It says that as believers, we have the mind of Christ. If wisdom is the ability to judge correctly and use our knowledge to avoid trouble, solve problems, reach goals, and succeed in life based upon God's principles, then having the mind of Christ is the key. Romans 12:2 says, "And be not be conformed to this world: but be ye transformed by the renewing of your mind." A renewed mind is the mind of Christ. And, we get the mind of Christ by reading His word, talking to Jesus, and asking Him for wisdom.

Colossians 3:2 reiterates this principle.

Write this verse here:

____

____

____

You may choose to continue to highlight verses of foolishness and wisdom for Part 2 of this study, but it is not mandatory.

Right Relationship with God

Lesson 40

"He that walketh in his uprightness feareth the Lord:
but he that is perverse in his ways despiseth him.
Proverbs 14:2

Let's get in a quick review from the very beginning of this course. Fill in the blank from Proverbs 1:7.

"The fear of the Lord is the beginning of ___________________."

Now check out Psalm 111:7-10.

"The works of His hands are verity and judgment; all his commandments are sure. They stand fast for ever and ever, and are done in truth and uprightness. He sent redemption unto his people: he hath commanded His covenant for ever; holy and reverend is His name. The _______________ of the Lord is the beginning of wisdom: a good understanding have all they that do his commandments: his praise endureth for ever."

What do you think the fear of the Lord is based on according to these verses – His terrible anger and desire to see men pay for their sins? Or His righteous justice and desire to see people repent and have a relationship with Him?

____

____

Psalm 112 will help you to answer that last question.

From Psalm 112, list some of the things that will happen to the man that fears the Lord. (I found 18.)

So, back to Proverbs 14:2 (See beginning of this lesson), what is the righteousness that man must walk in to fear the Lord? Job found out that it wasn't his own righteousness. He complained grievously before the Lord to come and hear his defense and then God would judge rightly. But when God did show up and ask a few questions of Job such as had Job

helped to lay the foundations of the earth? Who set its measurements? Or who enclosed the seas with a door? Or have you ever in your life commanded the morning, and caused the dawn to know its place? (Job 38-41). Job realized then that his righteousness was not enough to put him on equal footing with God to demand a response. He humbled himself before God.

> Listen to Job's words in chapter 42:2-6.
>
> "I know that thou canst do everything, and that no thought can be withholden from thee. Who is he that hideth counsel without knowledge? Therefore, have I uttered that I understood not; things too wonderful for me, which I knew not. Hear, I beseech thee, and I will speak: I will demand of thee, and declare thou unto me. I have heard of thee by the hearing of the ear: but now mine eye seeth thee. Wherefore I abhor myself, and repent in dust and ashes."

Fear of the Lord requires a humbling of the heart: a recognition of who God is; an understanding that we stand before God not in our own righteousness, but in the righteousness given to us to wear by Jesus as He died on the cross and took upon Himself our sin. It is the righteous in Christ that God refers to in Proverbs 15:29:

> "The Lord is far from the wicked: but He heareth the ___________
> of the righteous."

For "Who can say, I have made my heart clean, I am pure from my sin?" (Proverbs 20:9) Except those who have been cleansed by the blood of Jesus.

Many try to relate to God through church rituals and meeting expectations put on us by our parents or the church. But God is not impressed with ritual or sacrifice.

> Proverbs 15:8 states that "The __________________ of the wicked is an
> ___________________ to the Lord: but the prayer of the upright is his delight."

That's right, if you are born again through your faith in Jesus then God delights in you and wants to spend time with you and He enjoys the world that He made through you. And I know that He is looking forward to spending all eternity with you.

Listen to God's promise to believers in John 14:1-3: "Let not your heart be troubled: ye believe in God, believe also in me. In my Father's house are many mansions: if it were not so, I would have told you. I go to prepare a place for you. And if I go and prepare a place for you, I will come again, and receive you unto myself; that where I am, there ye may be also."

> In these verses what is the prerequisite for Jesus preparing you a place and
> coming back for you? _________________________________

Practical Proverbs

Did you have to tithe faithfully first? Offer a sacrifice? Do good deeds? No. All we have to do to spend eternity with God is believe (an action word) in God the Father and in Jesus.

If we fear God enough to believe His Word, we are going to heaven. Works and good deeds come after that in our gratitude and changed hearts and minds. God promises to be doing the changing in us for us. We have only to believe. God is so good!

Add pictures to Appendix C for Proverbs 3:19-20. Our God is amazing! Just look at the created world around you.

Now What?

Lesson 41

"Let the word of Christ dwell in you richly in all wisdom;
teaching and admonishing one another...
And whatsoever ye do in word or deed,
do all in the name of the Lord Jesus,
giving thanks to God and the Father by him."
Colossians 3:16-17

We learned in our last lesson that we can't work our way to heaven; that salvation comes only through believing in Jesus. So, now what?

At our house, when the kids were little, we had one overriding rule that took precedence over all others: "Did or will that make the other person feel special?" If an action did not make the other person feel special, then it was wrong. Colossians gives us an overriding rule for living a victorious Christian life: "Whatsoever you do in word or deed, do all in the name of the Lord Jesus..."

This is so important that it is stated a few verses later.

Write out Colossians 3:23. ____
____
____
____

That's right. We are to do whatever we do heartily, that means with a whole heart or effort, as for the Lord rather than men.

Notice in verse 17 that our actions should come from a heart of thanksgiving. What are we to be thankful for? Everything. First, our salvation. Second every breath that we breathe. Then, every action we can perform, every blessing we receive, and, yes, every trial that comes our way.

Read James 1:2-4.

Yep. We are to be thankful for the trials because they are working in us to make us perfect and complete.

It all narrows down to choices. How am I going to act in this situation? How am I going to respond to this circumstance? What is my attitude going to be like in this trial? How am I going to treat my body? How am I going to speak? How am I going to spend my money? My time? How am I going to let God work in my life to control my emotions? Am I going to read my Bible? Am I going to go to that Bible study or church? Who should I marry? What should I do for a career?

Boy, it sure would be easier if God just wrote it all out for us. I used to say, “God, just give me some writing on the wall like You did for Belshazzar.” (Daniel chapter 5). Then I realized that that very night, God took Belshazzar’s life and kingdom away. God does not spell everything out for us, because He wants us to have a relationship with Him. He wants us to talk to Him, share our hearts with Him, listen to Him, and obey Him. Finishing a list of to-do’s might be easier, but getting to know our Father and Savior is even better.

> Look back at our verses in Colossians. In Colossians 3:16 what must richly dwell within us? ____
>
> How must the Word of God dwell within us? ___________________________

What does that look like? It means that we are reading, studying, asking questions, memorizing, meditating upon and praying through the Word of God. It takes time, it takes commitment, but only through the Word shall we be transformed (Romans 12:2) and have the mind of Christ. (1 Corinthians 2:16). With the mind of Christ, according to Colossians 3:16, we will have wisdom and will be able to admonish and encourage one another.

These next lessons will help us to know how we are to walk and work doing all things for and through Jesus.

Review Proverbs 3:1-18 and work on memorizing verses 19 and 20.

Feeding Frenzy

Lesson 42

"I Beseech you therefore, brethren, by the mercies of God,
that ye present your bodies a living sacrifice,
holy, acceptable unto God,
which is your reasonable service of worship."
Romans 12:1

We read at the beginning of Part Two that God tells us, "Whatsoever we do in word or deed, do all in the name of the Lord Jesus." (Colossians 3:16). This includes how we treat our bodies. Let's see what the New Testament says about our bodies, and then we will get into some Proverbs about different bad habits.

Turn to 1 Corinthians 3:16.

This verse will give us a foundation for this study.

"Know ye not that you are a___________________ _______ ______________,
and that the Spirit of God dwelleth in you?"

This picture is repeated in 1 Corinthians 6:19-20.

"What? Know ye not that your body is a __________________ _______
___________ ______________ _____________ which is in you, which ye have from God, and ye are not your own? For ye are bought with a price: therefore glorify God in your body, and in your spirit, which are God's."

Let's think about these two verses for just a minute.

According to 1 Corinthians 6:20, why should we glorify God with our bodies?

____

What was that price? ____

That's right, the blood of Jesus paid for our sins and we are now no longer to be slaves to sin, but to righteousness.

And who is our righteousness? ______________________

First came the transaction, then the obedience.

List ways that you can glorify God in your body. Include do's and don'ts.

Hopefully your list included eating right, exercising, getting enough sleep, getting sunshine, not drinking alcohol, not doing drugs, not being a glutton, not having sex outside of marriage, etc. Are you going to obey? Let's see what Proverbs has to tell us about treating our body right. Let's start with our eating habits. Do you live to eat, or eat to live?

Think about that for a minute and fill in the blanks:
I ___________ to ______________.

Proverbs 25:16 warns us about overeating. "Hast thou found honey? eat so much as is sufficient for thee, lest thou be filled therewith, and vomit it." Honey is a nutritious food. It actually has healing properties within it. It is sweet and helps other foods to taste good. But even this food that is good for us can be eaten to excess and make us vomit. A good rule with food is "Everything in moderation." 1 Corinthians 6:12 is a great verse to memorize. Keep in mind as you read it that we are no longer under the law, but we have freedom under grace.

According to 1 Corinthians 6:12, what is lawful? ____________________________

Are these things profitable? ________________

The writer declares that he will not be mastered by anything. Are you mastered by your cravings and addictions to food? When you are anxious or angry or happy do you turn to food? Do you eat what is healthy to be a good steward of your body or do you eat what you want when you want it and allow it to be your master? There are varying degrees of misuse of food. For some it is an addiction to food, for others it might be cravings for sugary foods. We must ask ourselves if this food at this moment is profitable for my body. There are a lot of nutrition books on the market. Read a few. Learn about healthy eating habits. Decide now what you are going to eat and, some day, serve to your children. Healthy children eat healthy foods.

A few rules that our family has adopted about food are:

No white flour
No white sugar
No white rice
No pork

Most nutritionists agree on these four foods. We also watch for and exclude chemicals in our diet such as MSG and nitrites and nitrates. There are healthy substitutes out there. We try to eat living food (fruits and vegetables and whole grains) at each meal and have learned to reach for the raw veggies and fruit instead of the potato chips. That does not mean that we don't occasionally celebrate with ice cream and cake for birthdays or have an occasional

cookie, but we try to make the majority of our food choices healthy. The best way to start a healthy diet is to choose one or two things to eliminate or include. Don't try to live on celery and carrots which don't have enough nutrition by themselves.

Read a couple more Proverbs about honey and see what truths you can gain.

Proverbs 25:27-28 – What is a man who has no control over his spirit compared to?

____

Proverbs 27:7 – "The full soul (stomach is full and overflowing) loatheth an honeycomb; (that which is desirable and sweet and nutritious), but to a hungry soul every bitter thing is sweet."

Rewrite this Proverb in your own words: ______________________________

____

Remember, food is a gift from God to keep us healthy and to give us energy; it is not to be our god, nor is it to be abused and keep us from a full and victorious life.

Act out Proverbs 3:19-20.

Poisonous Pursuits

Lesson 43

"Wine is a mocker; strong drink is raging:
And whosoever is deceived thereby it is not wise."
Proverbs 20:1

God's Word is pretty plain about getting drunk or intoxicated. The same rules apply to smoking and illegal drugs. They are foolish. You have probably heard about the bad effects that alcohol has on a body. It kills brain cells, it is a depressant, it is addictive, etc. Let's see what else God's Word says.

Read Proverbs 23:20-21.

This Proverb goes one step farther and says that we should not even be with or associate with heavy drinkers or gluttons. Their fate will become yours.

What is their fate according to these verses? ________________________________

Check out James 4:4 and 1 Corinthians 15:33.

Summarize what these verses are telling you. ________________________________
____
____

Proverbs 23:29-35 describes the life of an alcoholic pretty well.

What is wine compared to in verse 32? ____________________

What are the results of too much wine? There are 10 listed.

1.	6.
2.	7.
3.	8.
4.	9.
5.	10.

Lastly, look at Proverbs 31:1-7.

Who should never drink wine according to these verses? ____________________

Who should drink wine? ____________________

These are strong verses. If you want to rule and have authority over your family, your employees, your kingdom, then don't drink wine for it will affect your decisions and judgments. If you are perishing and bitter, then go ahead and use alcohol to help you forget. Notice that it will help you forget, but it does nothing to turn things around, or bring you to peace.

Many Christians will point to Ephesians 5:18 and believe that a little wine is okay as long as you don't get drunk. I would like to point out though that we are to be filled with the Spirit and when we are filled with the Spirit of God there is no need for wine or strong drink.

I heard a Christian speaker say, "What the parents do in moderation, the children will do in excess." The fact that we want to be filled with the Spirit of God and that we don't want to ever give our children a negative role model has kept us to our pledge of no alcohol. If you never take the first step, then you will never follow down the wide road that leads to destruction.

James admonishes us to flee temptation. Don't be where people are drinking, don't try to fit in with the crowd who drinks, and don't believe that it can't happen to you and that you can handle just one drink. Most alcoholics used to believe the same thing. If you have sorrows to drown, take them to Jesus. If you have anger to work out, take it to Jesus. If you are depressed or down, take it to Jesus. He will comfort you and give you hope. Alcohol can't do that. If you need to celebrate, then dance and sing and shout joyful thanksgivings to God. Why take something that will depress you when you want to rejoice.? Illegal drugs fall in this same category multiplied by 10. Any substance that we rely on to try to fill the emptiness inside of us will only lead to death and destruction. Only filling up with Jesus will bring life and joy.

If you have taken a drink of alcohol or have gotten drunk before, take it to Jesus. He will forgive you and give you strength not to drink again. He may take away that desire immediately or He may want you to cry to Him when that desire overwhelms you. Either way He promises that He has provided a way out of all temptations.

> Read 1 Corinthians 10:13.
>
> "There hath no temptation taken you but such as is common to man: but God is ________________ who will not suffer you to be tempted above that ye are able, but will with the temptation also make a way of ________________ that ye may be able to bear it."

That's a promise. It is also a choice. For some it has to be a minute by minute choice because they have already fallen under the curse of alcohol. But for you, choose now never to go down that path and be freed from the torment and guilt that addiction brings. Cling to Jesus. He is enough.

Be ready to recite Proverbs 3:1-20 tomorrow.

Powerful Pride

Lesson 44

"Pride goeth before destruction,
and an haughty spirit before a fall."
Proverbs 16:18

The next several lessons will deal with the first and greatest temptation and sin – pride.

Pride is when we put ourselves before God. Pride is when we think that we are in charge. Pride is when we take the credit for something that we could not have done without the Lord. Pride was Satan's sin that got him kicked out of heaven. It was Eve's and Adam's sin that got them kicked out of the garden. We are saved by grace and won't get kicked out of God's family because of sin (see Romans 8:1), but we can be excused from God's presence. The fellowship with God can be broken.

Pride can seep into our worship, our dreams and goals, our memories, our actions, our words, our relationships. It is a heart-sin.

Look up Mark 7:21-23.

Listed among this infamous group of sins is pride.

Where do these verses say that pride comes from? ___________________________

Outward sins are usually the first ones that we point a finger at, but just as insidious and deadly are sins of the heart. Actually, outward sins are almost always the demonstration of heart-sins. James 1:14-15 says that temptation leads to lust and lust to sin, and sin leads to death. This is the LSD principle. Lust (your thought life), sin (your actions), death (the consequences). And don't think that sin for a Christian won't lead to death. We have eternal life with Jesus Christ, but this earthly life is still in peril as well as others' lives. May it never be that your sin would lead another to his/her death.

Recently, in the papers, we read about a public figure that got caught in adultery. He is a Christian and in an article in World Magazine says that his fall began when he thought that he didn't need accountability. He had several Christian men warn him to stay accountable to an individual or a group as he headed into public service, but he thought, "That won't ever happen to me. I can handle this." As he was tempted and his support group was not there to confront him, his lusts gave way to sin and will almost assuredly lead to the death of a marriage, death of trust, death of his job, death of respect. (Jaime Dean, "Giving Account", World Magazine, 07/2009).

So, let's look closely at this sin and see some examples, God's thoughts on pride, the results of pride, the opposite character trait of pride, and God's command about pride.

Satan's Downfall

Read Isaiah 14:12 -15.

Isaiah is prophesying here about Babylon and how Israel will glory in its fall. Prophesy, however, often has double meanings and many commentators believe that these verses also describe Satan's fall from heaven. Babylon is often associated with the world system which is Satan's realm.

Satan was the head archangel. His job was music leader. He was to lead the angels into worship of the Holy, Heavenly, Creator God.

According to Isaiah 14:11 what led to Satan's downfall?

____

Pomp is another word for arrogance.

In verse 13 we see the intent of his heart.

> "For thou hast said in __________ ____________, 'I will ascend into heaven, I will exalt my throne above the stars of God: I will sit also upon the mount of the congregation, in the sides of the north. I will ascend above the heights of the clouds; I will be like the Most High.'"

Satan began to think he was important and began to demand that others bow down and worship him. He thought that he was equal to or greater than God Almighty. The result of his pride is shown in verse 15: "Yet thou shalt be brought down to hell, to the sides of the pit." This prophecy has not yet been fulfilled.

Revelation 12:4 and 7-9 is also a depiction of Satan's fall from heaven to earth and how he took one third of the angels with him. He is reigning here on earth until the end of times when according to Revelation 20:1-3 he will be overthrown and bound and cast into the abyss for a time. Eventually, (Rev. 20: 10) Satan will be thrown into a lake of fire for eternity.

Satan was not satisfied with his downfall. He convinced one third of the angels to go with him. We call these demons. But he is not through yet. He desires to convince humans as well to follow after him rather than God.

Now, let's look at the first sin of mankind in the perfect garden and perfect relationship with God.

Adam and Eve's Downfall

Satan decided that if he couldn't rule in heaven, he would rule here on earth. After all, he wanted to be like God. In Genesis we find the first couple walking with God. All of their needs were met. They lived in a lush garden with all the green plants for food. They walked with God, up-front and personal. They were welcomed into His presence. Enter Satan, seen here as the serpent. He lies to Eve and claims that if she eats of the forbidden fruit of the Tree of the Knowledge of Good and Evil she will not die as God has said, but rather she will be like God. Sound familiar? Enter pride.

Eve lusts to be like God and takes the fatal bite. The consequence of her sin is indeed death, and death was brought to all mankind by her choice. Don't get prideful and think that you would have handled things differently. Each of us has made choices based upon the same heart-sin – pride.

Our Downfall

There are examples all throughout the Bible and history of men and women making fatal mistakes based upon pride – wanting to have more power and prestige than is their due. Nebuchadnezzar is one example. God humbled him with a mental illness.

David thought that he could stay home from battle and just be king. His pride led him to adultery and murder.

Hitler, Stalin, Mussolini, and the other statesmen of the WWII era all fell to pride and took millions of lives. The Roman Empire fell to the pride of the Caesars.

What has your pride cost you? ______________________________

Has it kept you from making a commitment to Jesus Christ? ______________

Has it brought heartache to your parents and severed their trust? ___________

Has it destroyed opportunities to serve God? ______________________

I remember a time when I knew that God was prompting me to tell a young couple about Him. My pride kept me from telling them the good news. I have many times since prayed that God used a more faithful follower to reach them. But what if they didn't hear the Word and die in their ignorance. My pride may have kept them out of heaven.

Each of us deals with pride. But it can be overcome to a great degree. It is a battle that we must take on minute by minute, day by day. When we stand in the presence of Our Eternal, Holy, Almighty God, all pride will vanish. Until then, we will look at ways to defeat it.

Perverted Pride

Lesson 45

"The fear of the Lord is to hate evil:
Pride, and arrogancy, and the evil way,
and the froward mouth I hate."
Proverbs 8:13

What are God's thoughts about pride? ______________________________________

First let's look at what God says about pride, arrogance, boasting, haughtiness, and trusting in ourselves.

In James 4:16, it says: "But now ye rejoice in your boastings: all such rejoicing is ________________."

Look up Proverbs 6:16-19.

God hates six things and seven things are an abomination to Him.

What is the first on the list? __________________.

That's pride.

Proverbs 21:4 says: "An high look, and a proud heart, and the plowing of the wicked, is _______________."

Does God take pride seriously? The Scriptures say that He hates pride.

Why do you think that is?

____

____

____

God created man in His own image. He knows how special each one of us is and He loves us. He created us to need Him and to have a vital relationship with Him. When we are trusting in our own methods, talents, goodness, etc., then we are denying our rightful place in God's creation. He has created us a little lower than the angels, but not above Himself.
2 Corinthians 3:5 reminds us, "Not that we are sufficient of ourselves to consider anything as of ourselves; but our sufficiency is from God." He is our breath, our life, our very being. We are to work with Him, but never forgetting that without Him we can do nothing. This applies to all men.

Look at John 1:3. “All things were made by him (Jesus); and without him was not anything made that was made.”

Look also at a couple of other verses that put our existence into perspective.

1 Corinthians 8:6: “But to us there is but one God, the Father, of whom are __________ things, and we ________ him; and one Lord Jesus Christ, by whom are __________ things, and we ________ him.”

Colossians 1:16 -17: “For by him were ______ things created, that are in the heaven and that are in earth, visible and invisible, whether they be thrones, or dominions, or principalities, or powers: _______ things were ___________ ______ him, and ___________ him. And he is before all things, and by Him ________ things exist.”

So instead of being prideful, we should be worshipping and thanking God for our very existence.

As born again Christians, how much more we should recognize pride as sinful. We did not save ourselves. We did not die for mankind. We can’t earn our way to heaven. It is only by God’s grace and mercy that we can have an intimate relationship with our very Creator. When we realize this and accept that all that we are and all that we have is from God’s hand, then there is no room for pride.

Let’s define pride. Pride is an exaggerated self-esteem – thinking more of yourself than what is true. This is hard to do when you remember that you are God’s child, His prince or princess. But, you are not God. You are not in charge. You are not on the throne, God is.

It is good to like yourself (Galatians 5:14: “Love your neighbor as yourself.”) It is good to feel approval for a job well done. It is good to go to bed knowing that you lived the best you could that day. But always keep in mind that you are because God created you. You have a relationship with Him because He died for you. You are able because He has given you specific talents, gifts, and purposes. Let thanksgiving be always on your tongue.

To finish up today’s lesson, look at Proverbs 25:27.

What are God’s thoughts about pride?

“It is not good to eat much honey, so for men to search their own glory is not glory.”

Now, you are probably wondering what eating honey has to do with pride, right? Honey is good for you. But too much honey can give you a bad stomachache. Feeling good about yourself is also good for you, but seeking your own glory will make you sick spiritually.

Proverbs 27:2 says: "Let another man praise thee, and not thine own mouth; a stranger, and not thine own lips." Seek to do God's will, to know Him, to be obedient to His commands, and He will lift up whom He lifts up and He will put down those whom He puts down. There is a lot of relief in this reality. I don't have to promote myself. I can trust God to open doors and shut doors and bring me to the mind of others in His time. I can concentrate on just being the best me in Christ that I can be. God will take care of the rest. Boy, that goes against the world's principles. But remember we are not of this world. We are of a better, more everlasting world. And we belong to the King of Kings.

Because God hates pride, He has placed a judgment on it.

Read Proverbs 16:5.

"Everyone that is proud in heart is an abomination to the Lord; though hand join in hand, he shall not be ________________________."

God further declares in Isaiah 13:11:

"I will cause the __________________________of the proud to cease, and will lay low the ____________________of the terrible."

Proverbs 29:1 describes a man who in his pride," hardeneth his neck" or becomes stubborn and prideful.

God shows His love by first offering what? ____________________ (1 John 4:10)

But suddenly, the prideful man will be broken beyond remedy for there is no remedy for pride. If man is not willing to repent and step down from the throne of his own life and let Christ rule in all areas, then there is no salvation, no remedy.

Add Proverbs 3:21-22 to Appendix C and get busy memorizing.

Honoring Humility

Lesson 46

"A man's pride shall bring him low:
But honour shall uphold the humble in spirit."
Proverbs 29:23

So if we are not to be proud, how should we position our hearts? What is humility? What does it look like? How do we live it out? Let's look to God's Word for the answers.

Read Romans 12:16

"Be of the ___________mind one toward another. Mind not __________ things, but condescend to men of low estate. Be not ___________ in your own conceits."

We need to break this verse down. First, humility is being of the same mind as other believers. This means not putting yourself above them in your own mind. A Christian should not look at other Christians in judgment, but rather in love. If a younger Christian doesn't have the knowledge or discernment that I have, I am not better, just farther along on the journey that God is taking me on. God may have a different journey for my brother or sister. My attitude, in this case, should be one of gratitude towards God that He has taught me and trained me so that I can discern and teach others. Humility is being grateful.

The next part of the verse talks about not being haughty in mind but associating with the lowly. Our thoughts should not be prideful. This will lead to our actions not being haughty but rather our reaching out to those less fortunate or who are not in the same place in their life journey as we are. We should be grateful, act grateful, speak gratefully, and demonstrate our gratefulness through service to others.

Finally, the verse ends with a good reminder: "Be not wise in your own conceits." It is possible to act humbly without being humble. But this is falsehood and will eventually reveal itself. If you squeeze a sponge with water in it, water will come out. If circumstances squeeze a person who has pride, pride will come out. It may show itself in anger, or self-pity, or arrogance. If a person of humility is squeezed, he/she will remain humble, forgiving, and kind.

When was the last time that you were squeezed by life's circumstances?

____

____

____

____

What was your response?

a.) hurt and anger
b.) self-pity
c.) arrogance
d.) humility and concern for others

There are a lot of promises from God's Word for the humble. Look these verses up and write down the rewards of humility.

Proverbs 22:4 ____

Proverbs 21:29 ____

Proverbs 18:12 and Proverbs 15:33 ______________________________
____

Your answers should have included riches, honor, life, a sure way (confidence), and more honor.

So, we see that God would desire us to be humble, that there is great reward in humility, but how do we grow in humility?

We saw from yesterday's lesson that the first attitude that we must adopt is proper positioning before the King of Kings. He is on the throne, we are not. Today we learned the second secret to humility – gratitude. Being thankful for all that God has given us and done for us – being thankful for the people in our lives, our circumstances, and for whom God made each of us to be. There are physical attributes or circumstances in each of our lives that we wish God would change. Being grateful for them instead of resenting them is a big step towards a humble attitude. Just accepting that God knew and knows what He is doing in our lives and that all things, good and bad, comes through His hands, can lead us into a grateful heart.

Proverbs 30:11-14 describes an arrogant, prideful man.

> "There is a generation that curses their father, and doth not bless their mother."

A humble person then would thank his father and bless his mother in word and in action.

> "There is a generation that are pure in their own eyes, and yet is not washed from their filthiness."

A humble person is quick to acknowledge when they are wrong and quick to repent to God for that sin.

> "There is a generation, O how lofty their eyes. and their eyelids are lifted up."

A humble person is content where God has placed him and satisfied with the fruits of his labors, not looking to others wishing to be something that he is not.

> "There is a generation, whose teeth are as swords, and their jaw teeth as knives to devour the poor from off the earth, and the needy from among men."

A humble man is not stepping on others to get what he wants, but rather he reaches down and helps those who are less fortunate or are younger.

So let's list some characteristics of a humble man.

1. Has a good understanding of his relationship with God
2. Is grateful
3. Blesses his mother and father in word and action
4. Acknowledges when he sins and is quick to repent
5. Is content and satisfied with his lot in life
6. Is giving and compassionate towards others

How do you compare? ____

____

Take some time in prayer to ask God to reveal to you any area that you are still prideful about and ask Him to make you humble. But beware, God answers our prayers.

Just a quick note about number 3. Some people have parents that are easy to bless and others have parents that are not respectable. If you are in the latter category, know that God will honor your efforts to be obedient and respectful even if you only get grief in return. We will cover this more in detail in a later chapter on parents.

Humble yourself and try to fill in the blanks for Proverbs 3:19-22.

The ______________ by __________________ hath founded the earth;
by _________________________ hath he established the ____________________.
By his ____________________________ the depths are ____________________ up,
and the ____________________ drop down the dew.
My Son, let not them _____________________ from thine ____________________:
keep ____________________ wisdom and ________________________,
So shall they be life unto thy ________________________,
and _____________________________ to thy neck.

Humble Heart

Lesson 47

"He that trusteth in his own heart is a fool:
but whosoever walketh wisely, he shall be delivered."
Proverbs 28:26

Today we will see the reputation that pride brings and some commands from the Lord about pride. But first, let's review.

What is the opposite of pride? _______________

List 6 characteristics of a humble man from the last lesson,
1.
2.
3.
4.
5.
6.

Here are some verses to look up:

Proverbs 11:2 "When pride cometh, then cometh _______________________: but with the lowly is wisdom."

Proverbs 14:16 "A wise man feareth, and departeth from evil: but the fool __________, and is ____________________."

Proverbs 21: 24 "Proud and haughty scorner is his name, who dealeth in proud ______________."

List some of the characteristics of a prideful man according to these verses.

1.
2.
3.
4.
5.
6.
7.

Practical Proverbs

Look back over your chart in Appendix A.

A Biblical fool does not recognize God and lives his life in reckless abandon to the final judgment. But a prideful man goes one step further and does not recognize God, but places himself on his throne as God. For him there is no hope. Our hope is in Jesus Christ alone and the only way to Jesus is through the humbling of our spirit to recognize our own inadequacies and the need of a Savior. Pride is the wall that stands in the way for many a man to come to Christ. As Christians, pride is the wall that keeps us from a deeper walk, a more intimate fellowship with our Lord and King. Pride comes from the prideful one, Satan.

It is a fine balance between loving ourselves as creatures of a wonderful Creator and worshipping ourselves as better than we really are. It is a lifetime battle. Pride can ruin a marriage, break the hearts of your children, leave you without friends, and keep you from the presence of God. Be quick to recognize your sins or mistakes and be quick to repent and apologize. Keep current on your confessions.

Lastly, there are some verses that are a command and will set you on your way to stand before men and kings as an ambassador to the Mighty King.

Proverbs 27:2 "Let another man ______________ thee, and not thine own mouth; a stranger, and not thine own lips."

Proverbs 25:6-7 – "Put not forth thyself in the presence of the king, and stand not in the place of great men: For better it is that it be said unto thee, ________________ _______ ____________; than that thou shouldest be put lower in the presence of the prince thine eyes have seen."

As you finish up this study of Proverbs and we look at other areas of our lives, keep in mind that pride is often at the root of all other choices.

Ask God to dig up any pride in your life and make your heart humble before Him.

Act out Proverbs 3:19-22.

Perfect Parents

Lesson 48

"Hearken unto thy father that begat thee,
and despise not thy mother when she is old.
The father of the righteous will greatly rejoice:
and he that begetteth a wise child shall have joy of him.
Thy father and thy mother shall be glad,
and she that bear thee shall rejoice."
Proverbs 23:22, 24-25

Your parents are not perfect. They are human beings just like you. They have dreams and aspirations, frustrations and failings, and good days and bad days just like you. Some parents are Christians and are trying to raise their children up in the fear and admonition of the Lord. Others have not come to the saving knowledge of Jesus Christ and are trying to raise their kids up the best that they can in human understanding. Either way, they are human and they will make mistakes and let you down.

As infants and small children, we all think that our parents are perfect. We want to be just like them. They are our first role models. Then as we grow and mature we begin to realize that they aren't perfect and that sometimes, we don't want to be just like them. What does the Bible say about how we should respond to our parents – whether they be good or bad parents? As we study these verses you will begin to realize that God does not put parents into separate groups of good and bad, but rather He expects us to honor them no matter what. That is hard.

How can a son or daughter honor an alcoholic dad or an abusive mom? Notice in the verse above that Solomon mentions the mother that gave birth to you. At the very least we should be thankful to our parents for giving us life. Mom went through an awful lot of pain to bring you into this world. For that you should honor her.

Most of us have parents that, at least, fed us regularly and gave us a bed and clothes to wear. For that be thankful and honor your parents.

Proverbs 20:20 says, "Whoso curseth his father or his mother, his lamp shall be put out in obscure darkness." If you have nothing positive to say about your parents, don't say anything at all. You honor your parents by not speaking badly of them. This is hard to do when other boys and girls are berating their parents. But you are accountable to a holy God who has given you His command to "Honour thy father and thy mother." (Matt. 19:19).

In Exodus 20:12 God tells the Israelites to, "Honour thy father and thy mother: that thy days may be long upon the land which the Lord thy God giveth thee." He restates this to His children of grace in Ephesians 6:1 when He says, "Children, obey your parents in the Lord: for this is right." He then quotes the verses from Exodus. So, obeying your parents is a way of honoring them. You should obey them not just in action, but in attitude. God will bless your response.

We are responsible; each of us, for how we respond to what life throws at us. As long as your parent is not asking you to do something against God's commands, then obey without question and with joy. If they ask you to do something that you do not think God would have you to do, then respectfully talk with them about it. If they won't listen, get a Christian adult that you trust to go with you to talk with them. If they still insist, then decide if obeying them would go against God's commands. If you make a stand, make sure that God would approve, that you are respectful, and that you are willing to suffer the consequences.

If a young lady goes to her parents and tells them that she is pregnant and her parents say that they want her to get an abortion, she should follow the above steps. As God would not have her kill the child, she may have to suffer the consequences and move out. Anything to save that life.

But, usually, parents' requests are not against God's commands, but against our wishes. For instance, I wanted to attend a Christian college. My parents thought I needed to be at a secular college where I could get a full scholarship playing softball. I chose to obey my parents. It was a hard time, but God taught me valuable lessons. My parents moved to another state, and there was a Christian university in their town. I injured my shoulder and couldn't play softball, so they allowed me to go to the college in their hometown where I met my husband. If I had followed my own desires, I would never have gone to that particular university, and there would not have been this marriage, five boys, and, perhaps, a lifetime of ministry.

Will your parents make you mad? Probably. Will they always give in when you want something? Probably not. Are they always right? Probably not, but they love you. They were given a mandate from God to raise you up. If you can't trust your parents, then trust your God.

From the text above, what two things can you do to honor your parents?

1.
2.

As long as you are in the home of your parents or reaping the rewards of their financial gifts, then you are to obey. When you have moved out and are supporting yourself or get married, you are no longer a child, and you don't have to obey, but you must always respect and honor them.

Let's look at some verses from Proverbs. Look up each verse and fill in the blanks. Girls, remember that God is speaking to and about you, also.

Proverbs 10:1 "…A wise son maketh a _________ father: but a foolish son is the ____________ of his mother."

Proverbs 27:11 "My son, be wise, and make my heart _____________, that I may answer him that reproacheth me.

Proverbs 29:3 "Whoso loveth ____________________ rejoiceth his father, but he that keepeth company with harlots spendeth his substance."
(Remember that in the Old Testament, harlotry was a symbol for sin, idolatry in particular.)

Proverbs 13:1 "A wise son ________________his father's instruction: but a scorner heareth not rebuke."

Proverbs 16:31 "The hoary head is a crown of _____________________, if it be found in the way of righteousness."
(Remember, even though your parents may not be up on the newest technology, or the newest use of the English language, they have had many more experiences and have gained knowledge and wisdom.)

Proverbs 23:15-16 "My son, if thine heart be ________________, my heart shall __________________, even mine. Yea, my reins shall rejoice, when thy lips speak right things."

According to these verses, how can a son or daughter make their parent glad?
____
____
____

Be ready to recite Proverbs 3:1-22 tomorrow.

Perfect Parent

Lesson 49

"He that wasteth his father, and chaseth away his mother,
is a son that causeth shame, and bringeth reproach."
Proverbs 19:26

Parents – you can't live with them and you can't live without them. Yesterday we looked at some verses that told us what to do to honor our parents.

1. Do not speak badly of them.
2. Obey them.

Today we will look at what not to do in order to honor them. The verse above says that you should not assault your father or drive your mother away. This would include verbal assault and physical assault. God is very serious about this. In the Old Testament the penalty for striking your father or mother was death. (Exodus 21:15). Why was God so adamant about this? Well, our parents are God's representatives on earth of Himself. He is our heavenly Father. We all tend to relate to God as we relate to our earthly fathers. (We'll talk more about that in just a minute.) God demands and requires us to honor Him, so He must insist that we honor our earthly parents as His representatives.

Describe your father: ____
____
____
____

If you have never known your father or he is no longer a part of your life write "absent."

Your father is human. If he is a loving, caring, gentle man, then you probably are able to accept God's love and gentleness. If your father is harsh, or judgmental, or only gives love with conditions, then you probably see God as demanding and judgmental. That is why it is so important to read the Word of God and get an accurate picture of our Heavenly Father. It may take someone years to be able to transfer the truths about God as Father from their head to their heart because of their misrepresentation of Him through their earthly father. But when they get to know the true character of God, they can have a Heavenly Father that they are no longer afraid of. They will be able to climb into His lap, sit at His feet, twirl in joy before Him, and repent, knowing He will forgive with compassion, and they can "bother" Him daily with their requests because He cares. Before someone gets to this point, they might be able to accept God as King, Lord, Savior, Creator, etc..., but they will have a hard time not cringing and shrinking away from Him in fear.

Let's see the true nature of our Father through Scripture. I love the picture that Psalm 37:23-24 presents:

> "The steps of a good man are ordered by the Lord:
> and he delighteth in his way.
> Though he fall, he shall not be utterly cast down:
> for the Lord upholdeth him with his hand."

What a great picture. Do you see it? Think of a father teaching his child to walk. The father is holding the hand of the little one. The father is taking great joy in his little boy or girl. Suddenly the child topples and falls. The father does not scold or get angry. No, I see him laughing and getting down on his knees and picking up the child, comforting him/her, setting her back on his/her feet and taking delight in the entire process.

I think that is how God relates to our "failures." To Him it is just a topple, a fall. He claps at us for trying, sets us back on our feet, holds our hand, and points us in the direction that He has already established for us. God delights in you. Take a minute and let that sink in. It doesn't matter what you have done, what you think you are, or even if you are involved in something right now that you need to repent of. God delights in you just because you are His child. He created you, He loves you, and He takes joy in you.

Matthew 6 contains the words: "Our Father which art in heaven." Then follows with what is known as the Lord's Prayer. Actually it is an example prayer of what we can say and ask of God. Verse 8 even reminds us that "For your Father knoweth what things ye have need of, before ye ask him."

You can't remember being an infant. But think about how an infant is taken care of. He can't speak or explain what his needs are, but the parent knows. When it is time to eat, he is fed. When it is time to sleep, he is rocked to sleep. When he needs to be cleaned, the diaper is changed. A cry may come to get the parent's attention, but the parent knows and is just waiting to be summoned. So it is with God. He knows your needs for love, affection, affirmation, healing, forgiveness, self-acceptance, food, clothing, etc. before you even ask. He is just waiting for you to summon Him. And He is delighted when you do.

How does this fit in with not assaulting your earthly parents? They are God's representatives. If you assault them, you have, in essence, dishonored Him. If you don't respect your mom and dad, then at least, treat them as God's representatives and don't curse them or assault them. Even better, forgive them. Wow. That one can be tough. But God's grace and love and forgiveness can lead someone to forgive a mom or dad who was never there, a parent who was abusive, a parent who belittled and angered their child, a mom who didn't teach her daughter about womanhood, or a dad that didn't teach his son about being a man or who didn't represent godliness.

Remember that no one has perfect parents and we each need to forgive our parents for their mistakes and shortcomings. Talk to God; ask Him to put that kind of forgiveness into your heart. What release. What freedom. What joy. Then you can accept a Heavenly Father's love and be His little boy or girl.

Proverbs 30:17 gives us another admonition. "The eye that ____________ at his father, and ________________ to obey his mother, the ravens of the valley shall pick it out, and the young eagles shall eat it." Gruesome, but effective.

Proverbs 28:24 says: "Whoso ______________ his father or his mother, and saith, 'It is no transgression'; the same is the companion of a destroyer."

This verse would indicate robbing them of their material goods, but we must be careful not to rob them of their dignity, their hope, their joy,

So be careful of your words and attitudes towards your parents. Instead of chiming in with friends when they are putting their parents down, find something positive to relate about your own parents or encourage your friends to respect their parents as God's representatives.

Here are a couple more verses to look up concerning the relationship that you have with your parents. Write a brief synopsis of each.

Proverbs 28:24 ____

Romans 1:28-32 ____

2 Timothy 3:1-5 ____

Ephesians 6:1 ____

Money Motivation

Lesson 50

"Two things have I required of thee...
Remove far from me vanity and lies;
give me neither poverty nor riches;
Feed me with the food convenient for me:
Lest I be full, and deny thee, and say, Who is the Lord?
or lest I be poor, and steal, and take the name of my God in vain."
Proverbs 30:7-10

Money. It's necessary. Is it evil? How much is enough? What should our attitude be about money? Is a poor man more spiritual than a rich man? Is it wrong to be rich?

Proverbs answers all of these questions, but a broader view at the Bible will also help us to clarify our answers. Over the next several lessons, we will be looking at God's Word and His attitude towards money.

As always, God looks at the heart of man. Are our motives pure? Do we want money for selfish gain? Is money a reflection of my worth? Is money just a means to accomplish God's purposes in my life?

Several verses in Proverbs give us some clues about how we should look at money.

Look at Proverbs 30:7-10 above. What two things did the writer of Proverbs ask God for?

1.
2.

Notice the balance. He doesn't ask for riches, but he does ask not to be poor. Let's examine some attitudes that are often related to having much money and attitudes related to not having enough money.

In the above verses, what was the temptation of the rich? ____________________

What was the temptation of the poor? ___________________________________

The rich realized that he was self-efficient and didn't need God, whereas the poor stole in order to live and by doing so went against the law of God. When we break the law of God we are in essence saying that we don't trust God enough to provide; we take the bull by the horns and depend upon ourselves. Isn't that the same thing the rich is guilty of doing?

Either extreme leads to denying God, God's power, God's provision, God's goodness, and God's love.

Practical Proverbs

In Proverbs 23:4-5 it says, "Labour not to be rich; cease from thine own wisdom. Wilt thou set thine eyes upon that which is not? For riches certainly make themselves wings; they fly away as an eagle toward heaven."

Matthew 6:33 gives us Jesus' perspective on what we should consider.
According to this verse what should we seek? ____________________________
What is the word "all" referring to in this verse? __________________________

If you are not sure, go back a few verses and read verses 24-25.

That's right. God promises us that if we focus on the things of the kingdom of God, that He will provide our needs – food and clothing. Are you going to trust Him?

Riches are fleeting. Ask someone who gained their wealth in the stocks and bonds of the 1920's. During the great crash of the 1930's, many went from top floor executives to basement bums. Many committed suicide.

Use the following chart and compare these verses:

	Those Who Trust in Riches	The Righteous
Prov. 11:28	will fall	will flourish
Prov. 15:16	________________	much treasure
Prov. 28:6	perverse	______________
Prov. 16:8	________________	righteousness
Prov. 11:4	no profit	______________
Prov. 10:16	________________	______________
Prov. 28:20	not be innocent	______________

We memorized Proverbs 3 in the first part of this study.

Verses 5-6 says to "Trust in the _____________with all thine heart; and lean not unto thine own understanding. In all thine ways acknowledge ___________, and he shall direct thy paths."

This includes your finances. We, as Americans, are so richly blessed that we forget to give God the glory and to depend on Him, but He is God of our finances as well as our souls.

Draw pictures for Proverbs 3:23-24 in Appendix C – almost done; hang in there.

More Money

Lesson 51

"The blessing of the Lord, it maketh rich,
and he addeth no sorrow to it."
Proverbs 10:22

How much money do you need to have enough? What amount will make you content? What must your salary be for you to be happy? These are all common questions and you may have a ready answer. But people across every economic level have found that "enough" is always "a little bit more." So they continue to pursue the dollars and never have "enough". Contentment is the key to financial success. Now, in everything there is the need for balance. Being content out of laziness is not going to bring happiness either. We will discuss work ethic and God ordained work in a couple of days. But today, let's focus on contentment.

Paul says in Philippians 4:11-12 that he has learned to be content in what circumstances? ______________________________________

Wow! The only way that that is possible is through the grace of God and through praise to Him in everything. Go back a few verses to Philippians 4:6. That's the key.

"Be careful for nothing; but in ___________ __________by prayer and supplication with ____________________ let your requests be made known unto God. And the peace of God, which surpasseth all understanding, shall keep your hearts and minds through Christ Jesus."

Contentment, then, is being at peace with God about every circumstance, trusting that He will take care of your needs.

We learned yesterday that we should first seek God's ______________________.

If we are truly walking in righteousness, having been born again through Jesus Christ, are truly seeking His kingdom, are walking in obedience in an intimate relationship with Him, and giving thanks to God in every situation then He will meet all of our needs. What a promise. What relief.

An important concept to learn is that we are to trust God. Period. We are not to trust that He will give us things, or do things for us, or change our circumstances. We are just to trust God. He knows all things and loves us and wants the best for us. We ask, but we may be asking amiss because we do not see the whole picture. If your faith is in God and not in what He will do for you, then when you are caught in the storms of life and circumstances don't turn out the way you want them to, you can still trust that God is in control and has a purpose and plan for all things.

While John the Baptist was baptizing in the desert preparing the way for Jesus, Messiah, several groups of people asked him what to do to prepare for the coming wrath. His response is found in Luke 3:11-14. He told those that had two tunics to share with those who had none, and for those with food to share with those who had none. He goes on to tell the tax collectors to be honest in their dealings and not to collect more than they are supposed to. To the soldiers he said not to take money from anyway by force and not to accuse anyone falsely.

> He also told them in verse 14 to "Be ____________________ with your wages."
>
> Hebrews 13:5 says, "Let your conversation be without covetousness; and be ______________ with such things as ye have: for he hath said, I will never leave thee, nor forsake thee.'"

Wealth is fleeting. If we put our trust in money, our trust will be broken. But, "Jesus Christ is the same yesterday, to day, and for ever." (Hebrews 13:8) Put your trust in Him and you will be forever taken care of.

Jesus never promises us wealth, rather He promises troubles and tribulation. Here is a "Treatise on Suffering" that I wrote when I was struggling with some hard circumstances.

> Why does God allow suffering in our lives? This has been answered a hundred times over in books, articles, sermons, etc. But, I believe that I have stumbled upon one of the best explanations that will take God off the hook, allows Him to be worshipped as sovereign and good, and brings hope to the heart of the sufferer. It all has to do with perspective.
>
> If we believe in a God who promises us a life of ease and comfort, health and wealth, then we are not following the God of the Bible. No, Jesus is realistic when He says that to follow Him we must take up our cross and follow Him. He says that in this life we will face persecution and troubles, heartaches and heartbreaks. He says do not be overcome by these troubles because we are not of this world. That's right it's about perspective of where we live. When Adam and Eve sinned in the garden, Satan was given dominion and authority over mankind and this world. He is the prince of the air, the lord of the earth. And the earth was given to every kind of illness, debauchery, decay, and heartbreak that man has ever known. We live in a garbage dump ruled over by the great deceiver. Living in a garbage dump will bring stink and decay. One cannot be in a garbage pit and not get garbage on them. It is in the very air that we breathe. One of his greatest deceptions is that as Christians we should be above our earthly dwelling and should experience only good and right and blessings.

So we go about expecting to live on cloud nine and become frustrated and unbelieving when we see the reality of our garbage dump. We coast along expecting good things to encounter our path and when something goes astray so does our faith. In reality we should expect nothing but garbage – we live in a garbage pit. Then when troubles come, we know where they came from, why they came, and how to endure through them. When good things happen, what a miracle. What a joy. What a reason for rejoicing. In times of illness or defeat, we look to our Savior who will one day remove us from the garbage pit and set us on cloud nine. But for now He promises His comfort, His wisdom to avoid some of the garbage from splashing on us, and His presence. And that is enough. In great pain, great loss, great confusion born of this world there is hope. Hope for the future (heaven) and hope for the minute by minute dealing with the trouble (His presence and comfort).

So when you lose your job, get sick, lose a loved one, face a giant, or are slandered or afraid, remember that when you live in a garbage pit, it stinks. But God sent His Son to give us a way out and a way through. He is faithful and kind. Look to Him.

How does this perspective differ from the traditional Christian perspective?

____

____

Learning to be content in the midst of the garbage dump takes supernatural power – power that comes only from a close walk with our Savior.

Act out Proverbs 3:21-24.

Wily Wealth

Lesson52

"There be four things which are little upon the earth,
but they are exceeding wise:
The ants are a people not strong,
yet they prepare their meat in the summer;
The conies are but a feeble folk,
yet make their houses in the rocks;
The locusts have no king,
yet go they forth all of them by bands;
The spider taketh hold with her hands,
and is in kings' palaces."
Proverbs 30: 24-28

When you think of majestic, proud animals does the ant, the coney (a small rodent like a chipmunk), the locust, or the spider come to mind? NO. When we think of majesty and power, we think of the lion, the tiger, the bear, and the elephant. And yet, God uses four of the smallest creatures to teach us a lesson about pride and provision.

When you think about powerful people, who comes to mind?

____

You may have written Donald Trump, Barak Obama, Oprah, or Bill Gates. These are people who have riches and power on the national scene. But are these godly, wise people that we should emulate?

God provides for the small creatures by giving them the instincts to survive. The ants know to store food for later, the conies know to build their houses in the rocks for protection, the locusts know to stay together for food, and the spiders are able to live in the palace of the king. If God loves us more than these, then He will provide our needs as well. And He does it in grand style.

When our family first moved to Fort Worth, Texas, to attend seminary, my husband was out of a job for about 8 months. We had three children at the time that needed to eat. God provided a part-time job for me at a preschool two days a week that met the some of the basic needs of our family and still allowed me to homeschool kindergarten with our oldest. We still had a house in North Dakota that we were making payments on as well. We had a garage sale one month and made $1 more than the house payment. When things got really bad, someone put some groceries on our front porch and another time there was money in the mailbox. To this day I do not know the donors of these generous gifts.

Christmas time came and there was no money for presents. We got a call to go and look in our car. Someone had put a few gifts for the boys in the front seat. Easter came and I needed hose. My secret pal from the preschool included a pair in a basket of Easter goodies. Throughout this entire time, we did not make our needs known to man; we simply prayed and waited upon the Lord. He is faithful and true. In recent years God has provided buyers for a house, college scholarships for three sons, and money for music lessons, and we have never missed a meal.

Wealth and pride often go hand in hand. Let me state here that God has given wealth to a few people that it might be used for his kingdom, but generally it is a little bit given graciously by many that makes up the vast amount of contributions to churches and ministries. "For unto whomsoever much is given, of him shall much be required." (Luke 12:48)

Here are a few Proverbs that reiterate this point.

> 28:11 "The rich man is wise in his ___________ _____________; but the poor that hath __________ ________________ searcheth him out."
>
> 18:11 "The rich man's wealth is his strong city, and as an high wall in his own ___________________."
>
> 10:15 "The rich man's wealth is his _______________ __________: The destruction of the poor is their poverty." (Remember our lesson on extremes. This is poverty born out of laziness.)

If a rich man puts his trust in his money and makes it his stronghold, his security, then it is a false security. This false security will lead to greed. "If I need money to be okay, then more money will make me more okay." And Proverbs 11:6 tells us what becomes of a greedy man. "The righteousness of the upright shall deliver them: but transgressors shall be taken in their own naughtiness." (NAS reads: "…but the treacherous will be caught by their own greed.") Greed is the opposite of contentment. Contentment is found in a grateful heart.

> Take a minute and list the things that you are grateful for.

1.	6.	11.
2.	7.	12.
3.	8.	13.
4.	9.	14.
5.	10.	15.

Can we trust the Lord to provide for our needs? Proverbs 10:3 reads: "The Lord will not suffer the soul of the righteous to famish…"

> Read what Proverbs 13:25 has to add; "The righteous eateth to the satisfying of his ____________: but the belly of the wicked shall want."

That pretty much assures us that God will provide for our needs of food and sustenance.

Practical Proverbs 

Now, for our need of shelter and a place to dwell. Proverbs 10:30 says that:"…the righteous shall never be removed: but the wicked shall not inhabit the earth." Proverbs 14:11 gives us confidence that: "The house of the wicked shall be overthrown: but the tabernacle of the upright shall flourish."

God is equipped to "Supply all your need according to his riches in glory by Christ Jesus." Philippians 4:19

We joke at our house when we have a financial need that God owns the cattle on a thousand hills (Psalm 50:10), and I hope He will slaughter and sell one for me.

Fill in the blanks for Proverbs 3:21-24:

My son, let not them ________________ from thine ____________________:
_________________ sound wisdom and _________________________,
So shall they be __________ unto thy ____________________
and ________________to thy _____________________.
Then shalt thou ____________ in thy way _________________________,
and thy_______________ shall not stumble.
When thou liest down, thou shalt not be ____________________:
yea, thou shalt___________ ________________,
and thy ________________shall be _________________.

Excellent Economy

Lesson 53

"He that giveth unto the poor shall not lack:
but he that hideth his eyes shall have many a curse."
Proverbs 28:27

Today we are going to look at God's economy. It is much different than the "take care of number one" philosophy of this world. Look at the following verses and fill in the chart.

	The world's way	God's way
Life	Cling to it	Matthew 16:24-25 ____________________ ____________________
Material needs	Get all you can	Matthew 6:33 ____________________ ____________________
Enemies	Get revenge	Matthew 5:44 ____________________ ____________________
Money	Get it, horde it	Matthew 6:19 Luke 6:38 ____________________ ____________________
Relationships	Independence	Matthew 18:3 ____________________ ____________________

As you can see, God's economy is not the same as the world's system. There are several references in the New Testament to giving away money or possessions in order to gain material needs or eternal life. Giving away our possessions will not gain us eternal life unless it is an outward sign of an inward change of repentance and faith. But many so cling to their material wealth for security that they must release it in order to gain a relationship with Christ. That is another premise of God's economy.

Sometimes we must let go of something in order to gain something better.

> What might be something that one must let go of in order to gain a right relationship with God? Here are a few examples to get you started: sins, dreams, time.

Now you add a few more.

____

____

I had a group of women do this at a retreat and we came up with about 50 different things that one might be asked to yield, or give up to God to gain a right relationship with Him.

Others included singleness, job aspirations, desire for a family, health, addictions, etc. These are things that we must relinquish the right to have or to be in control over, knowing that God has a plan for each of us and that plan may include or not include some of the things that we have set our eyes on. Does that make God a killjoy? Should I expect a life with no pleasures or desires? No, there are just different pleasures and desires that we can have. The greatest being the pleasure of spending time with a God who loves us deeply. Maybe God didn't give a woman the ability to have children, but instead she was able to adopt and nurture several orphans or abused children to maturity. God always has a plan for what we might consider our failures or shortcomings.

Let's focus in on money. It is necessary. But we should learn to be content with what God has allowed for us in the context of the work He has provided for us. Money should not be gained falsely, and what we have we should share cheerfully with others. Here are a few more Proverbs about giving to the poor.

Proverbs 29:7 "The righteous considereth the cause of the poor: but the wicked regardeth not to __________ it."

Proverbs 22:9 "He that hath a bountiful eye shall be blessed; for he giveth of his _________ to the poor."

Proverbs 21:13 "He whoso stoppeth his ears at the cry of the poor, he also shall cry himself, but shall not be__________________."

Proverbs 19:17 "He that hath pity upon the poor lendeth unto the ____________; and that which he hath given will he pay him again."

Proverbs 18:23 "The poor useth entreaties; but the rich answereth ____________."

Proverbs 17:5 "Whoso mocketh the poor reproacheth his_______________: and he that is glad at calamities shall not be unpunished."

Proverbs 14:31 "He that oppresseth the poor reproacheth his Maker: but he that _______________ him hath mercy on the poor."

Proverbs 11:25 "The liberal soul shall be made fat: and he that watereth shall be ___________________also himself."

Jesus gives a word about this in Matthew 25 in the illustration of the sheep and the goats. Read this story in Matthew 25:31-46. Again, eternal life is not gained by righteous acts, but rather those who know Jesus and have been changed by Him will desire to do good deeds for others and thus is an outward manifestation of an inward change. As Christians we are to be about taking care of those less fortunate whether they are there by their own hand or by their circumstances or by the sins of others.

Let's get practical. I see a man on a street corner begging for money. I don't know his story. My first reaction is that he probably brings in more money every year than I do. And there are panhandlers out there who make a good living. But I don't know. What does God say? Give, but use discernment. I might give him a sandwich or a bag of groceries. I will not give him money that he can use on alcohol. If he insists that he needs money for a doctor's bill, I can offer to go to that doctor's office and pay the bill.

We give to organizations that have a good track record of helping the poor. We avoid offers to help those that can't give an account of the how the funds are actually used. My husband has been in the ministry for many years. He will sometimes offer someone a job if they are really in need. It may be painting a wall or digging a ditch. If they are really in need they won't mind working for a couple of hours. Then the church has an agreement with a local gas station and grocery store. We give the needy person a voucher and they can get gas and food, but not cigarettes or alcohol. We are to give, but we should give responsibly. And don't forget to tithe to the Lord from your income.

Be ready to recite Proverbs 3:1-24 tomorrow. Wow! You've worked hard.

Money Matters

Lesson 54

"A false balance is abomination to the Lord:
but a just weight is his delight."
Proverbs 11:1

There are three business practices that are mentioned several times in the book of Proverbs. These are false balances, surety (usury), and borrowing. We will look at all three of these today.

False balances

In the ancient world, bartering was used for purchasing goods. I might have bartered a round of cheese for a vessel of wine. Later, weight measures were put into use to make sure of a fair trade. Still later, gold and silver became the means for exchange, and again they were measured by weight. Scales were two trays on a fulcrum. A certain item's price was determined by its weight. If a dishonest merchant balanced the scale so that the buyer owed more than was truly fair that was called false balances. This dishonesty goes against the very nature and character of God. "Jesus is the Way, the Truth, and the Life…" (John 14:6). Truth is the very essence of God. False balances go against the truth and is, thus, "An abomination to the Lord."

Read Proverbs 16:11. Why are scales and balances of concern to God?

____

____

God is concerned with every area of our lives. If we are "… a new creature" (2 Corinthians 5:17) in Christ, then we were remade from the inside out when we asked Jesus to be our Lord. We don't get to pick and choose the areas of life that we want Him to control. He wants to be in control of everything, because He loves us and knows that as long as we hold on to any areas, then we are not fully devoted to Him and we are trying to serve two masters – ourselves and God. So, our business practices are of concern to our Heavenly Father.

Read Proverbs 20:10 and Proverbs 20:23. These verses reiterate God's hatred of falsehood.

Surety / usury

"He that by usury and unjust gain increaseth his substance, he shall gather it for him that will pity the poor.
Proverbs 28:8

Surety is loaning money at interest. In the early days of the nation of Israel, loans were not for capital (money needed to start a business), but rather for daily necessities. The Hebrews were admonished in Deuteronomy 15:7-10 to lend to the poor. Read these verses and fill in the blanks.

> "If there be among you a poor man of one of thy brethren within any of thy gates in thy land which the Lord thy God giveth thee, thou shalt not __________________ thine heart, nor _____________ thine hand from thine poor brother: But thou shalt open thine hand wide unto him, and shalt surely lend him sufficient for his need, in that which he wanteth… Thou shalt surely give him, and thine heart shall not be grieved when thou gives unto him: because that for this thing the Lord thy God shall bless thee in all thy works, and in all that thou puttest thine hand unto."

God is concerned not with the gift, but the attitude and character of the giver. If you lend for the sake of earning money, then that is not a pure motive. We should lend that others might benefit. We should give out of love and compassion not out of selfish gain or ambition. Stewardship is a term that many Christians use when describing their relationship to their money. Money is not something that we possess, but rather something that has been given to us by God to be used for His kingdom. We are stewards or overseers of that money. It is our responsibility to use it wisely. When we realize that it is not ours in the first place, that it is God's, then we don't mind giving it back to God for His purposes.

Now, if you know any history of the Jewish people to the present day, you know that they are known for moneylending. Does this not go against the command of God? Good question. So glad you asked. Yes, it does. But the Jewish people first rationalized this occupation because they did not loan money to other Jews, only to foreigners. Both Jeremiah and Ezekiel condemned the practice of surety (Jer. 15:10; Ex. 18:13). But unfortunately this practice continued to thrive. After the exile, Nehemiah "set a great assembly against them." (Neh. 5:1-13)." (Davis Dictionary of the Bible – 477). The Romans' 12 Tablets laid out harsh punishment for those unable to pay a debt. By the time of Jesus, a regular bank had been set up in Israel. None of this, however, repeals God's commandment. His commandments are always based upon His character and His character does not change. Loaning money out at interest in wrong even today.

Borrowing

> "The rich ruleth over the poor, and the borrower
> is servant to the lender."
> Proverbs 22:7

Surety is strongly prohibited in Scripture, so borrowing, although not forbidden, is warned against. Either we trust that God will be our Provider or we take that role into our own hands. When we are in charge and aware of the world's system of credit, it is easy to justify borrowing money. We think that we can control the circumstances around paying it back. Unfortunately, we can't see the future, and events may come up that keep us from being able to repay a debt – a loss of a job, an economic slump in the national economy, other bills, etc. Even though Scripture does not forbid us to borrow, it does give us fair warning that if we borrow we become a slave to the lender until we can pay back the amount due.

> Proverbs 22:26-27 warns, "Be not thou one of them that strike hands, or of them that are ________________ for debts. If thou hast nothing to pay, why should he take away thy bed from under thee?"

Many good Christian organizations give advice against borrowing, but they also realize that in today's economy that buying a house would be impossible without a loan. There are smart ways though to borrow for a mortgage. Larry Burkett suggests that you save up for a large down payment, buy small, pay it off, then sell it and use the equity to purchase a bigger house which you should still be able to pay off quickly.

College loans are another issue in today's world. There are ways to get through school without incurring a great debt load. The first is hard work. My oldest son worked two 40 hours a week jobs during summer months and a part time job during the school year. Between that and scholarships, he was able to get through his first four years with only a very small debt that he paid off the next year working at the college. While he was working at the college, he was able to take Master level classes for free and finished that degree as well. He is now employed by the school lawyers and will be able to finish his law degree with no debt. He will be able to get a good job and pay for his doctorate as he goes.

Secondly, look for scholarships. They can come from unexpected sources. My third son wanted to get a degree in agriculture. He spoke to the agriculture teachers and found out that being a member of the livestock judging team comes with a good scholarship. Never having judged before, he is learning a lot and getting paid to do it.

Thirdly, look at cheaper options such as junior colleges and online courses. Dual or concurrent enrollment is free or very inexpensive in some states and can save you up to a year's tuition.

Hard work is usually the first answer to this difficult problem of borrowing. The second and equal answer is contentment. How much do you really need that new car, that bigger house, those fashionable shoes, etc…? Be wise and prudent. Be patient and save up for purchases. It will bring you much less hardship in the long run. And, you will see the hand of God work if you choose to wait upon His provision instead of trying to obtain things on your own.

Believable Budget

Lesson 55

"Commit thy works unto the Lord,
and thy thoughts shall be established."
Proverbs 16:3

This verse assumes that you have a plan (a thought). That is what we are going to talk about today – establishing and following a budget. A budget is a monetary plan. It is naïve to believe that if we make money and spend it without a plan, that everything will work out. Proverbs 14:15 puts it this way: "The simple believeth every word: but the prudent man looketh well to his going."

There are a lot of good Christian books on setting up a budget. The main thing is not the format, but that you have a budget and you stick to it. Budgeting is simply an exercise in writing down how much money you make and how you will spend it. To get started, write down any regular amounts that you receive such as a wage earned from a job, a regular birthday gift, or allowance. Then keep track for a couple of weeks what you spend your money on. Be reasonable. If you spend $40 on gas a week, don't budget $30. What you have on paper won't work unless it matches what you do in real life.

List below your income and expenditures. You can do it by month or year. When you are completely out on your own, it is best to have a yearly budget including those yearly expenditures such as Christmas, vacation, etc.

Income:
Job
Gifts
Allowance

____

Expenditures:
Tithe
Gas
Food
Car payment and maintenance
Entertainment
Clothes
Gifts
Toiletries
Savings

____

____

____

As you get out on your own other categories might include:

Medical expenses
Medical insurance
Life insurance
Electricity/gas
Water/sewage
Debts
Groceries
Home maintenance
Taxes
School supplies

And there should also be a miscellaneous category for unexpected things like postage, haircuts, and school supplies.

The total income should equal the total expenditures.

When I first started using a budget it was easier for me to actually have envelopes with headings on them for each category. I would then place the amount of money allotted to each category in the correct envelope. When I ran out of money in that envelope, I either didn't spend any more on these items until the next payday, or I shared from another envelope and paid it back the next payday. This was very effective. Sometimes I would run short in the same envelope month after month and I knew that I needed to change my budget. Now we are sophisticated and have a computer program that sets up our envelopes. But the concept is the same. It even spits out monthly and yearly reports so that we can manage our money wisely. We use Crown Money Map Financial Software. They even have an internet based program called Mvelopes that attaches to your various bank and credit card accounts. My son finds this a very effective way to see the big picture and be able to deal with the details.

Even with budgeting software, we need to keep on top of our budget. We spend about an hour a week inputting all of our receipts and balancing our checkbook. Payday usually requires a couple of hours to pay bills. So budget your time as well as your money and realize that the investment in time will bring great dividends.

> Luke 16:11 is a good reminder for us in how we use our money. "If therefore ye have not been faithful in the unrighteous mammon, who will commit to your trust the true riches?"

I have a friend that decided that she could stay home with her kids and save more money by couponing than by going to work. She has done just that. Her pantry is stocked, her kids are at home with Mom, and the bills are paid.

Begin memorizing our last two verses. Proverbs 3:25-26.

History of Work Habits

Lesson 56

"He that tilleth his land shall have plenty of bread:
but he that followeth after vain person shall have poverty enough."
Proverbs 28:19

Now that we know what to do with our money, let's look at how we earn or gain our wealth. There are many verses in Proverbs that talk about work ethic. Work ethic is the personal principles and character traits that you display when you are working. For example, diligence and honesty would constitute a good work ethic, while laziness and shoddy workmanship would make up a bad work ethic. We will be exploring both good and bad habits in the work place.

The first thing that we are going to look at concerning work is its history and origin. God assigned Adam work even in the Garden of Eden. In the perfect world before sin entered in, there was work to be done.

> Genesis 2:15 tells that God put the man into the garden to "...dress it and to ____________it."

His next job is found in Genesis 2:19-20 where Adam got to name the animals. These jobs were assigned even before Eve took that fateful bite. God created man to work.

When you think of work, do you immediately think of unpleasant tasks? I don't believe that work has to be that way. Work is meaningful occupation of your time. I love to work hard physically. Give me a tree to dig up or a garage to build and I am one happy woman. Some people prefer physical work and others mental work or social work. One kind of work is not better than another, although physical work does have added benefits such as a feeling of well-being because of chemical changes that it sparks in your body and keeping your body in shape and healthy. Most of us will find that whatever jobs we undertake will be a combination of all three kinds of work.

> God does not put a priority on kinds of work, but He does tell us in 2 Thessalonians 3:10-11 "...if anyone would not work, neither should he __________. For we hear that there are some which walk among you disorderly, working not at all, but are_________________________."

This is in line with Proverbs 28:19 at the beginning of your lesson.

God does not require that we work all the time, for He set aside $1/7^{th}$ of our time for rest. That is the purpose of the fourth commandment (Deuteronomy 5:12-13):

> "Keep the Sabbath day to ____________ it, as the Lord thy God hath commanded thee. Six days thou shalt labour, and do all thy work: But the seventh day is the Sabbath of the Lord thy God: in it thou shalt not do any work..."

Many years ago in communist Russia, it was decided that men were wasting time and money by working 6 days and taking the 7th day off. The government decided to go to a 10 day work week with the 11th day off. Production went down, men became sick, and missed more days, general morale became lower. They wisely went back to a 7 day week. The God who created us for work also created us for rest.

Balance is the key. Proverbs 21:17 reminds us that, "He that loveth pleasure shall be a poor man: he that loveth wine and oil shall not be rich." That is not balance. Balance says that he/she who works hard, plays hard. There is nothing wrong with well-earned rest. But there is everything wrong with laziness and slackness on the job.

A practical principle:

When at work, work.
When at play, play.

Remember that each of us gets better at the thing that we spend our time on. If you're balancing work and play 6/7th to 1/7th, then you will be the man or woman described in Proverbs 22:29: "Seest thou a man diligent in his business? He shall stand before kings; he shall not stand before mean men." For now, schoolwork is work. So is a part-time job, athletics can be, as well as band. Remember work is meaningful occupation of your time.

What type of work do you like to do best? Physical, social, or mental?

What type of physical work do you do?

What type of social work do you do?

What type of mental work do you do?

What do you do for recreation?

What would you say your work to play ratio is?

Draw pictures for Proverbs 3:25-26 in Appendix C.

Worthwhile Work

Lesson 57

"Prepare thy work without,
and make it fit for thyself in the field;
afterwards build thine house."
Proverbs 24:27

We talked before about having a plan for your money, called a budget. It is also good to have a work plan so that you are prepared for any contingencies that might occur.

Jesus is teaching in Luke 14:28-32 about salvation and he compares yielding all relationships and earthly possessions up to Him with two people who need to be wise planners.

Who are these two people?
1.
2.

The builder needs to have a plan before he builds and the king should plan before he sends troops into battle. Jesus is saying that as Christians there will be a cost to discipleship as well. That cost is relinquishing our rights of relationship to others and to our possessions. That does not mean we are to live penniless and alone. Rather, as we turn all things over to Jesus, He changes our hearts and gives us new relationships and teaches us to use those relationships and our possessions for His kingdom. Whatever we turn over to Jesus, He turns back to us in wonderful ways, ways that we may never dream, but always for our good.

Just as the builder and the king should have a work plan, so should we. Your work plan might include college or learning a trade. It might be setting up a business or working for someone already in business. There are long term plans and short term plans. Planning your schoolwork to get it all finished on time, planning out your garden, or planning a meal would all be short term plans. Deciding on your educational track would be a longer term plan as well as deciding where marriage and children will fit into your life. The important thing is Have a plan. Count the costs.

Every decision that you make will limit your later decisions. If you choose to go to medical school and finish six years of training, your choices have been limited to a career in the medical field. You would not be able to get a job as an engineer.

Commit each plan to the Lord asking for guidance, then go ahead and plan. Use the wisdom from Proverbs and the rest of Scripture to make Biblical decisions. Sometimes God gives us the freedom to make choices. When your mom asks you if you would like a chocolate chip cookie or an oatmeal cookie, she really doesn't care which you choose. She will be happy with either choice. In the same way our Heavenly Father gives us choices that please Him. As long as we are not breaking the moral code of the Bible, we are free to choose. Using wisdom, talking to Biblically wise people, praying, following your heart, looking at your aptitudes and desires, should all give you clues to what some of your decisions should be.

Does God have a specific plan for your life? I believe that He knows what choices you will make, He promises He will work all things out for our good, but that He does not have a plan "A" that if we fail to find it then we are living God's second best plan for us. No, we are in a relationship with Christ. As we walk with Him, He will reveal to us if there is something specific that we need to do. If not, then we are free to choose within His moral code.

Here are some practical questions you can ask yourself to help determine a course of action in any decision.

1. Does it follow God's moral code?
2. Is it something that I have desired to do?
3. Does it fit into the pattern of things that I have chosen to do in the past and have shown an aptitude for?
4. Will it lead me into a deeper relationship with Jesus?
5. What are my parents and other Christian leaders' ideas about this decision?
6. Have I prayed earnestly about this and feel free to make this decision?

If all these answers line up, then you are free to plan. Just remember that no plan is set in stone and that God often takes us down one path to get to a turn off for another direction. But until you feel God pulling you in a different direction, rest in your decision, enjoy the ride, and make sure you have counted the cost. Psalm 138:8 says, "The Lord will perfect that which concerneth me: thy mercy, O Lord, endureth for ever: forsake not the works of thine own hands."

Don't fret and worry over decisions. Do as Philippians 4:6 says and know the peace of Philippians 4:7.

What does Philippians 4:6 tell us not to do? ________________________________

What does this verse tell us to do? ____

What is the result from this obedience? ____________________________________

Keep memorizing – try putting some actions to verses 25-26.

Willing Worker

Lesson 58

"The hand of the diligent shall bear rule:
but the slothful shall be under tribute."
Proverbs 12:24

Now that you have a plan, forward ho. With all diligence. The only way that a plan can be successful is hard and diligent work, and Proverbs has a lot to say about diligence and laziness.

Look up the following verses and dig up the joys of diligence. Make sure you read the whole verse.

Proverbs 10:4 "…the hand of the diligent maketh ________________."

Proverbs 12:11 "He that tilleth his land shall be satisfied with ______________."

Proverbs 12:14 "…the _______________ of a man's hands shall be rendered unto him."

Proverbs 12:27 "…the substance of a diligent man is ________________.

Proverbs 13:4 "…the ______________ of the diligent shall be made fat."

Proverbs 14:23 "In all __________________ there is profit…"

Proverbs 27:18 "Whoso keepeth the fig tree shall __________ the fruit thereof: so he that waiteth on his master shall be ______________________."

Proverbs 28:19 "He that tilleth his land shall have plenty of ________________; but he that followeth after vain persons shall have poverty enough."

From these verses what would you say is the opposite of diligence? ___________

It is very clear from these verses that not only will the diligent prosper, but the lazy will have want. Let's look at a few more verses.

Proverbs 27:23-27 is a warning. What is not forever? ____________________

This truth should move us to diligence.

Proverbs 12:11 Someone who pursues worthless things lacks what?

____

Proverbs 10:5 The son who sleeps in harvest acts how?

____

Proverbs 24:10 "If thou faint in the day of adversity, thy strength is small."

Think about it. If you don't exercise and work out, you won't be ready for war; if you don't store up money or food for times of trouble, you won't have enough.

Proverbs 18:9 A slothful person is considered a brother or kin to one that is

_________________.

Proverbs 20:13 What does a lazy person love? ______________________________
What will that gain him? ______________________________

Proverbs 21:25-26 The result of one that is slothful is _____________________.

Proverbs 20:4 Again, the sluggard does without because he will not work.

Proverbs 19:15 What will an idle soul suffer? ____________________________

Proverbs 10:26 A lazy person is going to find himself friendless and without a job because, "As vinegar to the teeth, and as smoke to the eyes, so is the _____________ to them that send him."

How does vinegar taste? _______________________

Don't you want it far from you? That is how an employee looks at a lazy person. He is no good to the company, no good to himself, and no good to his family. Unfortunately, when someone chooses the path of laziness, they hurt others as well as themselves.

We are going to look at two longer passages about a sluggard.

Read Proverbs 24:30-34.

Remember I am a mom as I ask these next questions. "What does your room look like? Is it clean with all items put away? Or could it use some diligence? What about your car, your locker, your other possessions?"

Now read Proverbs 26:13-16.

Don't get into this bad habit of excuses. Do you really think that there was a lion in the road? No, he was just lazy and didn't want to do what he was supposed to do, so he made up an excuse. If you do make up excuses, I hope they are better than these.

What is the sluggard compared to as he turns upon his bed?

____

That's a good comparison. You will notice that a sluggard or lazy person has an awful lot of the traits of a Biblical fool.

One of our favorite verses is Ecclesiastes 9:10. It's a great verse to memorize. "Whatsoever thy hand findeth to do, do it with thy might."

Fill in the blanks from Proverbs 3:23-26:

Then shalt thou ________________ in thy__________ ____________________,
and thy_________________ shall not ___________________.
When thou __________ __________________, thou shalt not be __________________:
yea, ___________ shalt, lie down, and thy _______________ shall be sweet.
Be not ______________ of sudden ______________,
neither of the __________________ of the wicked, _________ it cometh;
For the Lord shall be thy __________________,
and shall keep thy______________ from being ______________.

Work and Wealth

Lesson 59

"The crown of the wise is their riches:
but the foolishness of fools is folly."
Proverbs 14:24

Let's talk about a very misunderstood and misused concept in church doctrine today. Many call it the "name it and claim it" doctrine. There are ministers in some churches and on the television that teach that if you have enough faith and if you are living according to God's commandments, then all you have to do is ask for a material blessing and God will give it to you. They believe that if your faith is strong enough then you can tap into God's resources at your discretion. There are many verses in the Bible that they quote that can be used to support their doctrine if they don't take the whole context of Scripture to task.

For example, Luke 11:5-13 begins with the story of a person who has a friend stop by late at night. He doesn't have any bread to feed to this person, so he goes to another friend and asks for bread. This friend was already asleep and says, "Trouble me not..." The parable goes on to say that the sleeping friend will get up and give bread to his friend at the door not because of the friendship, but because of the persistence of the friend wanting the bread. This parable is followed by a very well-known and often memorized verse: "And I say to you, Ask, and it shall be given you; seek, and ye shall find; knock, and it shall be opened unto you. For every one that asketh, receiveth; and he that seeketh, findeth; and to him that knocketh it shall be opened." The very next verses say that if a son asks a father for a fish, he won't give him a snake. If he asks for an egg, he won't give him a scorpion. Then,

> "If ye then, being evil, know how to give good gifts unto your children: how much more shall your heavenly Father give the ________________ ______________ to them that ask him?"

The parables would lead you to think that God is talking about meeting our material needs in the form of food. But He clearly states that it is the Holy Spirit that will be given when asked.

Think back over history. There were many sincere, faithful, believing Christians during the first 100 years of the church who were martyred for their faith. In American history some of the most faithful Christians were black slaves before and during the Civil War. There were Christians in Jerusalem when Titus overcame the town in 72AD and starved the people. During the Boxer Rebellion in China, it was Christian missionaries who lost their lives. Did these faithful few not ask for God's provisions for food, protection, etc.? Was their faith not strong enough? Or were their deaths due to the sovereign plan of a sovereign God?

Jesus tells us that in this world there will be persecution, but that He will be there with us through them all in the form of the Holy Spirit, just as He promises in Luke 11. There are

many accounts of martyrs throughout history that died in fire or by sword or bullet that smiled, reached toward heaven, or sang praises as death encompassed them. The Holy Spirit was there and He was enough. He was the only bread and nourishment that their souls needed.

So what does all of this have to do with Proverbs or work? Look again at the verse at the top of the lesson, Proverbs 14:24. "The crown of the wise is their riches: but the foolishness of fools is their foolishness." The riches that this and other verses refer to are the riches of His glory – His presence in a believer's life manifested by peace, love, joy, patience, kindness, goodness, faithfulness, gentleness, and self-control. These riches are stored up in heaven and are the riches that we can have no matter what our earthly circumstances dictate. We are to work diligently to provide for our families; we are to pray to God for our daily bread, and we are to store up riches in heaven.

Look up these verses and see what they say about riches.

Proverbs 15:6 "In the house of the righteous is much treasure: but in the revenues of the wicked is _________________."

Notice that wealth is contrasted with trouble. This wealth is the wisdom that comes from God and His Word.

Psalm 19:7-10 "The law of the Lord...the testimony of the Lord...The statutes of the Lord...the commandment of the Lord...the fear of the Lord...the judgments of the Lord...more to be desired are they than ______________, yes, than much fine gold: sweeter also than honey and the honeycomb."

Let's review Proverbs 3:13-15

"Happy is the man that findeth ____________________, and the man that getteth ___________________________. For the merchandise of it is better than the merchandise of ________________and the gain thereof than fine ______________. She is more precious than __________________: and all the things thou canst desire are not to be compared unto her (wisdom)."

Any wealth that the righteous, or Christians, have is because they applied wisdom to their situation, God provided, and they were blessed. But, the absence of wealth does not dictate the absence of wisdom or righteousness or faith. God's sovereignty and sovereign plan over mankind often means that where there is a wealth of wisdom and faith, there is a lack of riches. God does promise to meet our basic needs if we but ask. But we would be better served to ask for the Holy Spirit and His kingdom.

You did it! Be ready to recite Proverbs 3:1-26 tomorrow.

Work and Welfare

Lesson 60

"He that oppresseth the poor to increase his riches,
and he that giveth to the rich, shall surely come to want."
Proverbs 22:16

God's Word has much to say about the way we treat the poor. There may come a time in your life, even though you are working hard, that you won't have enough to meet the basic necessities of life. As I write this, the unemployment rate is 10.9, which is very high. Even many that are working have taken major pay cuts or are only working part-time jobs. Those with college degrees are vying for jobs that normally high school graduates would fill. By God's grace, my husband still has work. But there was a time when he couldn't find a job for about 8 months. As I told you in a previous lesson, God provided miraculously during this time and our faith was strengthened. So, be thankful when you have plenty, realizing that is from God's hand, be humble, and give to the poor. 1 Samuel 2:7 is a good reminder.

> "The Lord maketh _____________ and maketh ____________: he bringeth low, and lifteth up."

Be careful of a judgmental attitude that may creep in when dealing with the poor. But also be discerning.

> Psalm 82:3-4 tells us to "Defend the poor and fatherless: do _____________ to the afflicted and needy. ______________ the poor and needy: rid them out of the hand of the wicked."

We do have a responsibility to give to the poor. I would suggest that this is the poor that cannot help themselves due to age or disability, not those who are depending on government welfare due to laziness or habit. These we can best help by giving them job skills. The truly poor, especially orphans and widows, we should defend, provide for, and help. This year at Christmas our MOPS group (Mothers of Preschoolers) has adopted a family of a single mom and two small children. The mom is working and trying to provide, but there is just not enough to pay the monthly bills, let alone anything else.

Proverbs 22:22-23 says "Rob not the poor, because he is poor: neither oppress the afflicted in the gate: For the Lord will plead their cause and spoil the soul of those that spoiled them." So, not only are we to give to the poor, we are to be careful not to rob the poor. This would include making sure that your business practices do not take from others who don't have. We are responsible for our money as well as our actions. Does your insurance company pay for abortions? Does the non-profit organization you support pay for drugs for the addicted? Does building that new high rise put people out of their homes? Does hiring an illegal alien for cheaper wages mean that a legal citizen is out of work? God does care about our business practices. And He promises to bless those who work righteousness.

Then there are the poor who are poor due to their choices, and Proverbs has something to say about them as well.

> Proverbs 19:7 "All the ___________________of the poor do hate him: how much more do his ___________________ go far from him."

This is a warning to keep you from wanting to be lazy and, thus, poor. Now, back to God's economy of giving. Proverbs 11:24 says that

> "There is that _____________________, and yet increaseth; and there is that _____________________more than is meet, but it tendeth to poverty."

The world teaches that to have we must hoard and to give would make us want. But God is sovereign and He says to give, and He will bring the increase. The story about R.G. LeTourneau says that he decided to test God on this principle. He decided to up his tithe to 12%, then 15%, and eventually to 90%. He became a very successful business man inventing and patenting over 300 earth moving machines and he founded a Christian college and a camp and conference center. He had more than enough and gave at least half away. The Mayo brothers who founded the Mayo Clinic gave 50% of their income away.
Lastly, Proverbs has something to say about money gained by fraud.

> Proverbs 13:11 "Wealth gotten by vanity shall be _____________________: but he that gathereth by labour shall ____________________."
>
> Proverbs 15:27 "He that is __________________of gain troubleth his own house: but he that hateth gifts shall live." (This refers to brides given as gifts.)
>
> Proverbs 11:18 "The wicked worketh a ___________________work, but to him that soweth righteousness shall be a ___________reward."
>
> Proverbs 10:2 "Treasures of wickedness profit nothing, but righteousness delivereth from____________."

That's God's perspective, again. What is riches compared to eternal damnation? Better the poor on earth who will live eternally with Jesus.

> Proverbs 28:22 "He that hasteth to be rich hath an evil eye, and considereth not that __________________shall come upon him."
>
> Proverbs 22:16 "He that oppresseth the poor to increase his riches, and he that giveth to the_______________, shall surely come to want."

A final encouragement: God says in Proverbs 13:22 "A good man leaveth an inheritance to his children's children: and the wealth of the sinner is laid up for the just." God will take care of His own. Trust in Him to provide, but put your hand to the plow and you will live a life of greatest riches (stored up in heaven).

Keep reviewing Proverbs 3:1-26.

Wise Words

Lesson 61

"Let the words of my mouth,
and the meditation of my heart,
be acceptable in thy sight,
Oh Lord, my strength and my redeemer."
Psalm 19:14

Proverbs has a lot to say about the words that we speak and the intentions of our hearts. Actually God addresses this issue throughout Scripture. Jesus speaks of the connection between the heart and the mouth in Matthew 12:34: "…for out of the abundance of the heart the mouth speaketh." He continues by explaining that "A good man out of the good treasure of the heart bringeth forth good things: and an evil man out of the evil treasure bringeth forth evil things." And He sums it all up with these words: "But I say unto you, that every idle word that men shall speak, they shall give account thereof in the day of judgment. For by thy words thou shalt be justified, and by thy words thou shalt be condemned."

Our words must be awfully powerful. Our words are just a mirror of our hearts. If we are seeking to live for Jesus, spending time in His Word, and trying to glorify God with our words and our deeds, then our words will justify our hearts' intentions. If we are living for self, trying to get ahead even if we hurt others, looking out for number one, etc. our words will condemn those heart attitudes.

Circle the following statements that mirror a heart that seeks to please God.

Well done.	You are so special to me	I love you
Way to go.	Can't you do anything right?	I am God's precious child
I am no good.	I can't believe you did that, you, moron.	You, idiot.

Make sure your words to yourself and others are truth – Biblical truth. God thinks you are a delight and He loves you.

You will need to work on memorizing Proverbs 18:21. This is a key verse.

Write this verse out below.

____
____
____

What does it mean that life and death are in the power of the tongue? Those are very strong words. What God is telling us is that we can offer words of encouragement that will lead to life for our listener, or we can speak words of death by degrading our listener. Remember that words are spoken not just to others, but to us as well. What does your self-talk sound like? Are you speaking works of life or death to yourself? Satan is ever the deceiver and will put words into our heads. He doesn't speak in third person "You are no good.", but rather in first person, "I am no good. God can't love me." That is why 2 Corinthians 10:5 tells us to "…take every thought captive to the obedience of Christ." In other words, look at every word that we speak or think and make sure that it lines up with the Word of God. God says that you are the Apple of His Eye, that you are fearfully and wonderfully made. If Satan is telling you otherwise it is time to tell Satan to take a hike. You must be in the Word to know what God thinks about you. Then don't let anyone or Satan tell you otherwise.

Proverbs holds so much about the tongue for good and evil that we are going to make a chart contrasting the two. Then we will tear it apart and look at some specific uses of the tongue that God says is fit only for the fool.

Use the chart below and on the following pages to list what each verse says about the tongue, words, lies, etc. Place your answer under the correct heading.

	Righteous man	Biblical Fool
Prov. 10:6		
10:10		
10:11		
10:14		
10:18		
10:19		
10:20		
10:21		
10:31		
10:32		

Wise Words (2)
Lesson 62

Continue your chart from yesterday.

	Righteous Man	Biblical Fool
Prov. 11:9		
11:13		
12:6		
12:13		
12:14		
12:22		
12:25		
13:2		
13:3		
13:5		
14:3		
14:5		
14:23		
14:25		
15:1		
15:2		
15:4		
15:7		
15:14		

15:23

15:26

15:28

16:13

16:21

16:23

16:24

16:28

17:7

17:9

17:14

17:20

17:28

Wise Words (3)

Lesson 63

One more day to fill in the chart. You are doing great.

	Righteous Man	Biblical Fool
Prov. 18:4		
18:6		
18:7		
18:8		
18:13		
18:20		
18:21		
19:1		
19:5		
19:9		
19:22		
19:28		
20:15		
20:17		
20:19		
20:20		
20:25		
21:6		
21:23		
21:28		
22:10		

22:11

22:14

23:15-16

24:28-29

25:11

25:12

25:13

25:14

25:15

25:18

25:23-24

26:2

26:18-19

26:20

26:21

26:23

26:24

26:25

26:28

28:23

29:8

29:20

Work on memorizing Proverbs 18:21.

Wordy Words

Lesson 64

"He that keepeth his mouth keepeth his life:
but he that openeth wide his lips shall have destruction."
Proverbs 13:3

Look over the charts that you have spent the last three lessons putting together. Write a four paragraph paper contrasting the mouth and words of the foolish or ungodly to the mouth and words of the righteous (those saved by the grace of God).

The first paragraph should be an introduction with a good thesis statement explaining what your purpose is and some words that grab the readers' attention.

The second paragraph should tell us what the words of a righteous man look like and their results.

The third paragraph should tell us about the words of the foolish man and their results.

The fourth paragraph will conclude the paper with a wrap up, a statement of the thesis statement and possibly your commitment to be aware of what comes out of your mouth and why.

Don't forget to review Proverbs 18:21.

Perfect Performance

Lesson 65

"If any man offend not in word, the same is a perfect man,
and able also to bridle the whole body."
James 3:2

The third chapter of the book of James has much to say about our tongues and our ability to control our words. Let's take a closer look at James 3:1-12. But don't get discouraged, there is an answer.

James starts off this chapter with a warning for teachers and overseers. He says, "My brethren, be not many masters, knowing that we shall receive the greater condemnation." (3:1) This verse assumes that there will be a judgment for our actions and our words. Jesus tells us in Matthew 12:36-37,

> "But I say unto you, that every idle word that men shall speak, they shall give account thereof in the day of judgment. For by thy words thou shalt be ________________, and by thy words thou shalt be _____________________."

Remember, we learned in lesson 58 that the mouth only speaks what is in the heart. Jesus places a pretty important emphasis on our words because they relay what is really in our hearts. If we are going to teach, we had better make sure that our hearts are right and that the words that we speak are from God.

James compares the tongue to three things, a bridle in the mouth of a horse, a rudder on a ship, and a small fire that sets a bigger fire burning. Let's look at these three comparisons.

James starts by comparing our tongues to the bridle in a horse's mouth. If you have ever ridden a horse, you know that he is bigger and stronger than you are and that he could throw you or brush you off. We even had a horse try to go under the barn door to scrape off its rider and another that threw itself to the ground to rid itself of its rider. Horses are dangerous unless they have been broken and trained. But even then, they can revert back to their old ways.

So how does a man control this massive beast? A bridle consists of a piece of metal bar about six inches in length that is attached to leather straps on each end. The rider puts the metal bar into the horse's mouth and holds onto the leather straps. When he wants the horse to stop a quick jerk on that bar tells the horse he better stop or it will hurt. A slight pull on the right strap will guide the horse to the right and a slight tug to the left strap will move the horse to the left – all to avoid a pinch in the mouth. So, an animal weighing 1000 – 2500 lbs. can be guided by a mere 6-inch bar and some leather straps.

James uses another comparison – that of a ship and its rudder. The average ship runs from 700 – 900 feet long and weighs several hundred tons. A rudder is a flat piece of metal hooked to the back of this hulking machine that turns the whole beast to the right or left.Notice in James 3:4 that James says that the rudder directs the ship wherever the inclination of the pilot desires.

The key verse is James 3:5. Write it out. ____
____

Here you see our third comparison. – The tongue is a fire that sets a larger blaze a burnin'.

The next three verses say that the tongue is evil and can't be tamed. That's pretty discouraging. But remember, even though we may not be able to tame the tongue, the tongue is only the speaker, the amplifier, of the heart. If you allow God to change your heart, then your tongue will spring forth with words of Godly wisdom and blessing. Remember, we change our hearts by letting God's Word be implanted there. Psalm 1 tells about a tree firmly planted by streams of living water. According to the second verse that tree is the man that plants himself near the Word of God and constantly, daily drinks in its wisdom and truth and life. Where are you planted?

Read the following verses and notice the relationship between the tongue and the heart.

Proverbs 10:20 – "The ________________of the just is as choice silver: the _________ of the wicked is little worth."

Proverbs 15:28 – "The _______________ of the righteous studieth to answer, but the ______________ of the wicked poureth out evil things."

Proverbs 22:11 – "He that loveth pureness of _______________, for the grace of his __________ the king shall be his friend."

Proverbs 23:15-16 – "My son, if thine _______________ be wise, my heart shall rejoice, even mine. Yea, my reins shall rejoice, when thy __________speak right things."

Proverbs 26:24 – "He that hateth dissembleth with his ___________, but he layeth up deceit within him."

And in these following verses notice the relationship between knowledge (of God's Word and way) and the mouth of the foolish.

Proverbs 11:9 – “An hypocrite with his _____________destroyeth his neighbor; but through _____________ shall the just be delivered.”

Proverbs 10:14 – “Wise men lay up _______________, but the ____________ of the foolish is near destruction.”

Let the words of your mouth be Proverbs 3:1-26. Recite it out loud.

Keep working on memorizing Proverbs 18:21 also.

Last Word on Words

Lesson 66

"Lying lips are abomination to the Lord,
But they that deal truly are His delight."
Proverbs 12:22

We are going to take this last lesson on the tongue and talk about probably the most widespread infraction of the mouth – lying.

In court in the USA the person being questioned is asked to "Tell the truth, the whole truth and nothing but the truth." What do these three phrases mean?

Well, to tell the truth means to tell what really happened or was said. Telling the truth means not telling a falsehood or making up a story. To "tell the whole truth" means that we will tell everything about the situation, not leaving out any details. At our house we say that a half truth is a whole lie. And "nothing but the truth" means that not only will we tell the truth, but we won't add anything false to the truth.

Then there is the "little white lie". When the phone rings and it is someone that you don't wish to speak to do you tell your sister or brother to tell them that you are not home when you are standing right there? Do you tell your mom how delicious her tuna casserole was when you really couldn't stand it? Some people justify a little lie saying that it will spare the feelings of another person.

> But God's Word says in 1 John 2: 21 "No lie is of the __________________."

> 1 John 3:18 goes on to say that we are to "Not love in word, neither in tongue; but in deed and in _______________."

Your reputation depends upon it. Do others speak of your truthfulness? Can they depend on you for your honest response?

When are you tempted to tell a lie? ____

Does your heart condemn you for the little fibs? _________________________

> 1 John 3:21 says, "Beloved, if our heart condemns us not, then we have _________________ before God." If we are truth tellers, then we are pleasing to God.

There are times that telling the truth will not yield you the greatest benefit financially or relationally, but God is pleased. You can lift your head high knowing that you followed

God's commandments. And looking back you may see that getting what you thought you wanted would have turned out to be a very bad thing.

I love the story that Corrie Ten Boom tells in her book, *The Hiding Place*. Her nephews were teenagers at the time of WII in the Netherlands. The Nazis would conscript any boy of fighting age and press them into the German army. One day the soldiers knocked on Corrie's sister's door and demanded that they hand over the boys. Corrie and her sister said that they didn't see the boys anywhere. Her sister began to laugh hysterically and say that they were under the table. The soldiers lifted the floor length tablecloth to no avail. The sister continued laughing and insisted that they were indeed under the table.

Corrie began to think her sister was crazy, because she was telling the soldiers the truth. Under the table was a rug. Under the rug was a trap door. Under the trap door huddled two very frightened teenage boys. When the soldiers finally left, Corrie asked her sister, "How could you?" She replied that she had been taught not to lie. She knew if she told the truth then God would protect her and the boys from the soldiers, and He did.

Let God be your confidence and your shield. Speak the truth in love and let God fight any battles that will come.

The words of a true friend are truth. Don't measure friendship by the way the other person makes you feel, but rather by whether he/she tells you the truth about yourself, your character, relationships, etc. That is a friend that will stick closer than a brother. (Proverbs 18:24)

Write out how you might be tempted to respond to the following situations and how you should respond.

1. Your girlfriend asks you if you like her new dress. You think it is very ugly.

   How you are tempted to respond:

   How you could tell the truth in love:

2. Mom asks whether or not you picked up the groceries she asked you to pick up on your way home from school. You forgot.

   How you are tempted to respond:

   How you could tell the truth in love:

3. You stayed out later than you had permission to because none of your friends had such an early curfew.

   How you are tempted to respond:

   How you could tell the truth in love:

4. Your friend wants you to get your ears pierced but you really just don't want to.

   How are you tempted to respond?

   How could you tell the truth in love?

Stop and think before those lies come out of your mouth. Are you telling the truth, the whole truth, and nothing but the truth? Are you willing to suffer the consequences of your actions? Do you want to stand in confidence before God?

Check out a couple more verses in Proverbs about lying; God is pretty specific.

Proverbs 26:28 – ____

____

____

Proverbs 26:18-19 – ____

____

____

____

(This is a good one to memorize.)

Proverbs 25:18 – ____

____

____

Proverbs 21:28 – ____

____

____

Proverbs 21:6 – ____

____

____

Proverbs 20:17 – ____

____

____

Proverbs 19:9 – ____

____

____

Proverbs 14:25 – ____

____

____

Think before you speak. Listen twice, Speak once. Check out Proverbs 10:19 and write a brief synopsis. ____

____

Ruinous Rage

Lesson 67

"He that is slow to wrath is of great understanding:
but he that is hasty of spirit exalteth folly."
Proverbs 14:29

This verse has a partner verse in the New Testament: James 1:19-20

We are to "Be swift to _________________, slow to _____________, slow to ___________: for the wrath of man worketh not the righteousness of God."

Let's talk about anger for a minute. Anger is the natural response that we have towards being hurt. It might be an emotional hurt or a physical hurt. The old saying that "Sticks and stones may break my bones, but words will never hurt me," is as false as anything. Words can hurt and do hurt. Whether the anger comes from abuse, a misunderstanding, or expectations that are too high, anger is a gift from God.

You are probably thinking, "What?" How is this rage and desire to get even, this hurt and depression, this overwhelming need to cry and to be understood from God? God created each of us with emotions. Emotions in and of themselves are not good or bad. How we respond to the emotions can be a problem however.

Anger is a warning sign to us that we have been hurt. Anger is a neutral emotion that comes from God. Even God gets angry so the anger is not the problem. It is when we allow anger to become sin that we have a problem. Anger is an emotional reaction that comes in the face of hurt. By expressing the anger that someone feels toward someone or something, most people are standing up for themselves – they are trying to drive home the idea that the deserve to be treated correctly.

Anger is a way of saying, "Notice my needs." God created within each of us two needs: the need for love and affirmation. We all need to feel worthy and significant. When these needs are not being met or are being threatened, we get angry. Anger can start out as a signal and a method of self-preservation, but turn into a pattern of destruction. This destruction can be turned on others or ourselves.

Look at Ephesians 4:26. Anger is neither good nor bad. This verse says

"Be ye angry, and _______________ not."

The anger is not the problem; how we handle our anger can be. Use your anger as a positive motivator to be used in giving one another feedback about how life can be lived more productively. In other words, communicate why you are angry and help to come up with a plan to solve the problem that led to the anger. There are two ways to communicate your anger: destructive and constructive. Let's look at a chart of these two responses. The following information came out of The Anger Workbook by Les Carter.

Destructive or aggressive anger	Constructive or assertive anger
Seeks to punish person	Seeks to help person who does wrong
Does not care about the other person's point of view.	Tries to be understanding
Is stubborn, immovable, and demanding.	Is flexible and willing to seek alternatives.
Is condemning and judgmental.	Recognizes we all have faults.
Has high expectations of everyone.	Knows even the finest people sometimes make mistakes.
Cares about what happens to oneself.	Cares about the welfare of others.
Holds grudges.	Knows the value of forgiving.
Does not notice one's own areas of weaknesses.	Recognizes that one can always improve.

Use your anger to solve a problem; don't escalate the situation with unwise words or actions. Think first, speak second.

Here are a few good ideas to practice when communicating.

Before you communicate:
1. Do not attempt to establish your own superiority
2. Make sure anger is constructive
3. Be aware of responsiveness of recipient
4. Consider feelings and circumstances of recipient (timing is everything).

As you communicate:
1. Discriminate essential from non-essential problems.
2. Confront problems as soon as possible.
3. Stick to the subject.
4. Be honest about your feelings (I statements).
5. Avoid terms of exaggeration.
6. Refrain from character assassination.
7. Listen to understand
8. Give yourself a time limit. (Don't carry on 2 hour lectures.)
9. Don't ask loaded questions.
10. Keep a positive attitude.
11. Be tactful about when and where
12. Remember that winning is not the goal.

Practical Proverbs 

Proverbs 12:18 will help us to remember to control our angry responses.

> "There is that speaketh like the piercings of a_______________:
> but the tongue of the wise is ______________."

Tomorrow's lesson will give us some practical steps to using our anger productively.

Acting Out Anger

Lesson 68

"He that is soon angry dealeth foolishly:
and a man of wicked devices is hated."
Proverbs 14:17

Yesterday you learned that anger is not sin, but what we do with our anger can be. So how do we control our anger?

1. You need to acknowledge the hurt. Pain, hurt, and anger are real and it is good to admit these things and the depth of the hurt. Find someone that you can talk to. If not a parent or sibling or friend, then find a Christian counselor that will listen and give Godly feedback.

2. You must grieve the hurt. Give yourself permission to be sad about the loss or hurt whether it is a loss of relationship, respect, or circumstance. The hurt is real and you need time to work through the grief process. This may include a physical release through walking or shooting baskets, etc. and an emotional release – speaking the emotions out in a respectful manner to someone who you trust.

3. You must give our hurt to God. Even if it is God with whom you are mad. He is big enough to handle your anger. Let Him know and talk to Him. God is the God of comfort (2 Corinthians 1:3-5). We will talk about forgiveness tomorrow, but remember that God has forgiven you and requires that we forgive others. God is bigger than any circumstance. He will carry it for you.

   Read 1 Peter 5:6-7: "Humble yourselves therefore under the ____________ hand of God, that He may exalt you in due time: Casting all your care upon him; for he _______________ for you."

   And remember that Matthew 11:28 carries a great promise. Write that promise here. ____
   ____

4. You must release the person that you are angry with to God for God says, "To me belongeth vengeance, and recompense." (Deuteronomy 32:35).

5. You are then ready to speak rationally about the situation. This might include strategizing your response, choosing healthier boundaries for a relationship, or confronting the offender with "I statements – "I felt disrespected or unloved when you said or did …").

What happens when we don't follow these steps and we let anger reign in our hearts? Anger can turn into bitterness, then into malice, then wrath, hatred, revenge, and eventually lead to multiple problems like destructive behavior, psychosomatic illness, suicidal ideation, and depression.

Bitterness is "characterized by intense antagonism or hostility," according to Dictionary.com. Bitterness is like drinking poison and hoping the other person will die from it. Bitterness hurts only you not the object of your hurt or pain. The writer of Hebrews warns us about not letting bitterness take root in our lives.

> Hebrews 12:15 says, "Looking diligently lest any man fall of the grace of God; lest any ___________of ____________________ springing up trouble you, and thereby many be defiled."

When that root takes hold, it is painful but necessary to dig it up. It would be better to deal with your anger before it can lead to bitterness.

What trouble might follow if you give in to bitterness?

Malice – the desire to harm others or do mischief; evil intent
Wrath – violent anger; fury
Hatred – seething fury turned towards the destruction of another
Revenge – actually carrying out the evil intents of the heart

Yes. Anger is best dealt with quickly. Back to Ephesians 4:26-27

> "Be ye angry, and sin not: let not the _________ go ______________upon your wrath: Neither give place to the devil."

If you are suffering from destructive behavior, psychosomatic illness (migraines, anorexia, tiredness, etc…), suicidal thoughts, or depression, then it is likely that your emotional bucket is full and overflowing. Let me explain.

We all have a capacity for emotions – our bucket. Some have a thimble sized emotional bucket; others have a mop bucket sized emotional bucket. If we allow the emotions of the past to fill up this bucket because we have not resolved them, then something relatively minor might happen and all of the sudden our bucket tips over and we are like an angry volcano spewing forth all the pent up anger and hurt. We need to keep that bucket on empty so that we have reserve emotional space when there is a new hurt. For me to empty my bucket I had to go back to things that happened a long time ago because I had repressed those memories and feelings. Just by talking them through, choosing to give them to Jesus and letting Him be the Lord of my past, and forgiving those who had hurt me, my bucket got empty and oh. The joy that swept in and filled me up. The sun was brighter and the circumstances in my life became clearer and the people dearer. Now I keep that bucket close to empty by talking things out as they happen.

Express your anger by communicating effectively and constructively and then release it. On this outline of a train engine and a caboose you see the word *Emotions* in the engine with *Truth of God's Word* following behind. What's wrong with this picture? ______________

____

____

There's going to be a train wreck. In this next picture the word *Emotions* is behind the engine and *Truth of God's Word* is leading the way. Now we will get there. God's Word lasts forever; our emotions come and go and come and go. Don't let your emotions lead you or drive you, rather hold tight to the Word of God, believe His promises even when they don't seem to be true, and give Him thanks and praise. Your emotions will get on board. Let your emotions be that warning light to make you stop and think about what was said and done, but then react as God would have you. Often the key to getting over a bad mood or depression is to sing praises. It's hard to keep frowning when you are thankful for what God has done. Give it a try.

Fulfilling Forgiveness

Lesson 69

"There is a way which seemeth right unto a man,
But the end thereof are the ways of death."
Proverbs 14:12

This verse can apply to many things in our lives, but it definitely is true about whether to hold a grudge and become bitter or to forgive. The world says stay angry; you have that right. But Jesus says that we are to forgive one another (Matthew 6:14). Let's look at that verse a little closer.

> Matthew 6:14-15 – "For if ye forgive men their trespasses, your heavenly Father ______________also forgive you: But if ye forgive not men their trespasses, ________________ will your Father forgive your trespasses."

Boy, that's something to think about. On a scale from 1 – 10, how important is it to God that you forgive others? 1 2 3 4 5 6 7 8 9 10 (circle one)

That's right, a 10. Now this can be a little confusing because we received forgiveness of all of our sins when Jesus died on the cross for us and we chose to believe in Him and be born again. I believe what this is saying is that when we became born again and received the Holy Spirit into our lives, we received the power and desire necessary to forgive others. If we don't want to forgive, then we haven't truly experienced God's forgiveness.

Remember the parable of the king in Matthew 18:23-35? He forgave a man a great debt, but that man turned to his neighbor who owed him little and demanded repayment and when he couldn't pay he threw him in prison. The king then came to the first man and he was handed over to the torturers with these words: "Shouldest not thou also have had compassion on thy fellowservant, even as I had pity on thee?" Then Jesus adds to this parable: "So likewise shall my heavenly Father do also unto you, if ye from your hearts forgive not every one his brother their trespasses."

Forgiveness is a journey. Remember the train in yesterday's lesson? We must first turn over the anger to God and stand on His word. He will comfort us. We must believe that everyone will be punished in the end who has not confessed Jesus as Lord. God can handle the vengeance part; we are to forgive. The emotions will follow as we ask God for wisdom and strength to forgive someone who has hurt us. There was a time in my life where I forgave someone who had hurt me very deeply. I told God every day for months that I had forgiven her. But I still cried every time I said her name. I didn't feel like I had forgiven her. But through time, my heart turned tender towards this person and I knew that God had done a work in my heart and that forgiveness was complete and the hurt had healed. Eventually, God called on me to go back into a relationship with this person, love her, and to be her friend. I was able to do so joyfully, but cautiously at first. Now I can wholeheartedly serve this person and love and accept her.

This is important. Highlight it. FORGIVENESS IS NOT ABOUT NOT HAVING NEGATIVE EMOTIONS ABOUT SOMEONE, OR ABOUT HAVING GOOD FEELINGS ABOUT SOMEONE, BUT RATHER RELEASING THEM FROM AN OBLIGATION FOR A DEBT. Forgiveness is not an emotion; it is a choice of your will.

When something happens and we have been hurt and are angry then we tend to say things like, "Boy, she sure owes me an apology." There is a debt there. We feel that the one who wronged us owes us to make it right. Forgiveness is canceling that debt and setting the other person free. This does not mean that there shouldn't be boundaries put on the relationship, but it does mean healthy, honest communication.

There comes a time when we need to forgive someone whom we cannot confront because of death or because of the other person's anger. In times like these it is helpful to either write a letter to that person pouring out the depth of the hurt and the fact that you have chosen to forgive, or find a friend or counselor to talk through the pain and hurt and let them know that you are choosing forgiveness. You don't have to mail the letter. Show it to a friend, talk it out with a counselor, and then burn it or rip it up. I even had a group of ladies that were in Bible study because of abuse in their past that wrote the name of their abuser on a helium balloon and released it to God. As we watched those balloons soar away, they were able to let go of the hurt, forgive their abusers, give it to God and begin to heal.

Forgiveness requires a humbling of the heart – a recognizing of my guilt before the Lord. Even as a Christian, I struggled with this because I was and had always been a fairly good person. By man's standards, I wasn't so bad. A lot of my anger was because I had been the victim. But when I got serious about dealing with my past, God humbled my heart and showed me my sins, my sinful attitudes, my self-reliance, etc. With this humbling came a greater appreciation for what Christ had done for me. He, too, had been a victim, but He forgave and demands that we, too, forgive.

Les Carter has written two great books on forgiveness: *Choosing to Forgive* and *The Forgiveness Workbook*. The following ideas and tomorrow's outline are from these books.

> Forgiveness is the willingness to let go of self-harming or ineffective forms of anger, choosing instead to turn over the ultimate resolution of the wrong to God.
>
> Forgiveness is the act of setting someone free from an obligation to you that is a result of wrong doing against you.

Tomorrow we will look at excuses people give not to forgive and what forgiveness does and doesn't mean.

Bitter Battle

Lesson 70

"A merry heart maketh a cheerful countenance:
but by sorrow of the heart the spirit is broken."
Proverbs 15:13

Nothing will make a heart sad and break the spirit like unforgiveness. Remember, if we don't forgive, then bitterness will take root in our hearts. And bitterness is like a poison to our souls.

Yesterday we also learned that if we don't forgive others, then God won't forgive us. He wants us to be free from bitterness and anger that we might be able to lead a cheerful and joyful life.

We are going to look at some lists from Les Carter's books about excuses people give not to forgive.

Reasons people won't forgive:
1. "I'd just be sending the message that he/she can do wrong and get away with it."
2. "This would mean I've got to bury my anger."
3. "If I forgive it means the other person wins and I lose."
4. "I guess I'll just have to put a smile on my face and say everything's all right."
5. "I feel that I'm being required to go soft on something that's severely wrong."
6. "One more time I've got to play the good-guy role while the bad guys just skip on their way."

Let's talk about a couple of these. #1 and #5 put the person in the place of judge and jury over the wrong doer taking on the responsibility to make sure that the person is judged and can't just get away with it. There are times that we need to tell someone in authority about someone's actions, because these actions will put this person in further danger to themselves or others. These circumstances would include knowing that a person is drinking alcohol, doing drugs, doing something illegal, cutting, or threatening suicide, putting others at danger, perhaps reckless driving, etc. If any of these situations is the case, then you have a duty to that person to seek help from an adult or person in authority. But your communication should be constructive, not vindictive. Forgive that person, feel sorry for that person, and let God do a work in their lives. It is not your responsibility.

Numbers two and four – Repressing or burying anger is not dealing with it properly. That's ignoring it. And that won't make it go away. Release your anger through the steps we set out in lesson 68. Then you can put it behind you and look ahead. If you bury it or repress it, it will come back and haunt you.

Look at Philippians 3:13-14.

> "Brethren I count not myself to have apprehended: but this one thing I do, _______________those things which are behind, and reaching forth unto those things which are before, I press toward the mark for the prize of the high calling of God in Christ Jesus."

For years, I thought that that meant literally to forget the hurts of the past and move on. I tried for 25 years to keep looking forward and to press on. I made a lot of headway, but there was always a discontent and depression lurking in my heart. When I faced my past and forgave those who had hurt me, then I could truly put it behind and move on. Before, I was not forgetting so much as burying, repressing, ignoring it. Forgetting is in the progressive tense which means that we are to be about forgetting. If the hurt were a big bonfire, you would turn your back to it and begin walking, running, or crawling away from it. As long as you are making progress away from it, then you are forgetting.

Numbers three and six are martyr's excuses. Poor me. I always have to say I am sorry first. He wins, I lose. The good guy (me) gets the shaft. Okay, that may all be true, but God says that we are to humble ourselves, to serve others, to forgive. This won't make you a lesser person, but a bigger man (or woman). We don't lose; we win with a heart at peace with God. The circumstances may make others think that the other person won, but eventually, as we walk around cheerful and joyful and the other person is full of remorse and hate, they will realize that we are the true winners. And if not, that's okay too because we should be about pleasing God, not man.

Read 2 Corinthians 5:9-10.

What should our ambition be? ____

Who will appear before the judgment seat? ______________________________

What will be judged there? ____

As Christians, we will be allowed into the kingdom of God (heaven), but there is also a judgment for us according to our deeds. We will be given crowns based upon our motives and deeds that we, in turn, will place before Jesus. I don't have time here to go into this study, but there are 5 crowns mentioned in the Scriptures. You may enjoy researching this further on your own.

I would add one more excuse to the list above. "He or she didn't apologize or ask for my forgiveness." Yes, it's easier to forgive when the other person realizes the hurt they've caused and apologizes, but Jesus died for us while we were yet sinners. (Romans 5:8).

Sometimes the person that hurt you won't ask for forgiveness. At times like this, you must remember that we forgive in obedience to God and to keep our own hearts from bitterness.

Forgiveness Finished

Lesson 71

"When a man's ways please the Lord,
he maketh even his enemies to be at peace with him."
Proverbs 16:7

God is on His throne. He can change the hearts of men. Our responsibility is to live with integrity before the Lord; He will provide for us and protect us. It all goes back to trusting in the Word of God and in the Lord.

Let's look at some misunderstandings that people have about forgiveness.

Forgiveness does not mean:

1. Letting go of healthy forms of anger.
2. Allowing others to continue to disrespect your needs and boundaries.
3. Lying down and becoming a human doormat.
4. Telling the wrongdoer that the past is no longer significant and everything's fine now.
5. Agreeing to become best buddies with the wrongdoer.
6. Pretending to go back to normal relations as if nothing happened.
7. Denying that you may still have to live with pain caused by the wrongful deed.

Forgiveness does mean:

1. You will let go of the demand for repayment, particularly as you have exhausted all reasonable attempts at restitution or restoration.
2. You will free yourself to focus on rewarding relationships and pursuits.
3. You will choose to give up any obsessions regarding the wrongdoer, recognizing, instead, that you have better things to give your attention to.
4. You will be willing to refrain from the ongoing temptation to insult the wrongdoer.
5. You will let go of any illusions that you might somehow control the wrongdoer's life.
6. You will be forward-looking about life, realizing that new opportunities await you.
7. You will give yourself permission to make life choices that will lead to contentment and peace.

Part of my forgiveness journey was the fear of having to stay in a relationship with the person who hurt me. When I realized that forgiveness did not mean that I would have to put myself back into an unhealthy relationship, I was able to take another step towards trusting God. Boundaries are necessary in any relationship. The Bible never says to forgive and forget. God forgives and forgets our transgressions and throws them as far as the east is from the west, but we are not asked to do so. It is healthy to remember past abuses, learn from them, and not put yourself in a relationship that will repeat them. A battered wife who divorces her husband and marries another wife-beater hasn't remembered. A sexually abused child that abuses another or gets into a relationship with another abuser, doesn't remember. We should remember so that we can put healthy boundaries on our present relationships. When I forgave, trusted God, and put healthy boundaries on the relationship with the one who hurt me, I was able to learn to love and be with this person. He has changed and, praise God, so have I.

Remember that Philippians 3:13-14 said that I was to put the past behind and reach forward? Well, that is what forgiveness allows you to do: to look to the future with expectation and joy.

Is there anyone that you need to forgive right now for big things or little things? Take a few minutes and lay this situation before God choosing to forgive rather than demanding that you be repaid.

Responsible Rearing

Lesson 72

"Train up a child in the way he should go:
And when he is old, he will not depart from it."
Proverbs 22:6

Even though you are probably not raising children yet, you might someday and you will want to train them up in wisdom. I have heard a lot of sermons on this verse. Let's look at what this verse doesn't mean then we will look at what it does mean.

First of all, this verse does not mean that if you pound Bible verses into a child's head, he will never sin. This verse does not mean that if you decide that a child should be a doctor and train him in medicine that he will be a doctor. This also does not mean that if train a child in righteousness, pray for them daily, take them to church, etc., that they won't go their own way for a time. Remember salvation is an individual choice. However, if you raise a child in God's Word and pray for them daily it is very likely that eventually they will return to the teaching of their childhood and become a Christian living a righteous life.

What this verse does mean is that each child has a natural bent, a God given personality. If you, as the parent, train them up in the way that they, personally, should go within that personality and with wisdom from God's Word, then they will not depart from it. If your child is compassionate and caring, artistic and creative then don't insist that they take technical drafting. Rather let them explore the arts or the healing crafts. If your child builds cathedrals with his blocks that are ornate and technical, you might encourage him to be an engineer or lawyer. Take the next 18 years and help him/her to explore the different careers that are available within his/her interests. Don't belittle or degrade a child for what, by nature, he/she enjoys. But let boys be boys and girls be girls. God did create them uniquely different. Help them to celebrate that difference and revel in who God made them to be.

Some children are readers, others are doers. Each child has a learning style, how they interpret their world. Are they visual, audio, kinesthetic, or oral learners? My visual learner was an early reader. My kinesthetic learner could learn anything if he did a project with it. My audio learner is doing great in college where he shows up for classes and listens to the lectures. An oral learner may need to talk out loud to process the information that he is learning. There are a lot of books on learning styles.

Some children have different learning weaknesses as well. My dyslexic children really have a hard time spelling. We work on spelling and introduce typing and spell check early. My ADHD child needs rigid structure for safety and to process. My visual learner needed a lot more assignments or else I would find him hiding a reading book behind his math book. Learn your child. Some are right brained and some left or whole brained. Right brained children are artistic and random; left brain children are technical and literal. One makes great

interior designers and the other will do well in accounting. Right Brained Kids in a Left Brained World by Jeffrey Freed (Simon & Schuster, 1988) is an excellent book for any parent. There is so much out there on biblical parenting – become an expert.

My experience as a mom, a Sunday School teacher, as a staff wife at various churches, and as a friend is that choosing to put young children in a public school setting for 8 hours a day and then taking them to church for 2 hours on a Sunday is not sufficient training to raise godly children. We must train our kids not only in their bent and according to their learning styles, but we must train them in righteousness. This takes consistency and hard work. A family devotional and prayer time in the morning, personal Bible readings, and a Biblical lesson at night as well as in the course of each day is the minimal that it will take to ground your children in God's Word. Don't assume the church, the youth group, the Christian school, etc. is doing your job for you. These precious little ones are your responsibility as a parent and nothing can replace that.

Read Deuteronomy 6:7. When should you teach your children? ________________
____
____

Remember that being an example is a much better teacher than just telling your kids what to do.

Totally Together

Lesson 73

"Better is a dinner of herbs where love is,
Than a stalled ox and hatred therewith."
Proverbs 15:17

One of the most important decisions that you will make in the next ten years or so will be whether to get married or not and to whom. Let's look at what a relationship with the opposite sex should look like in each of the following stages of a relationship.

Timothy was a young man that Paul the Apostle took under his wings and trained. In the book of 1 Timothy, Paul is giving Timothy some suggestions on relationships that will help align his heart with God's and keep him free from impurity.

Look at 1 Timothy 5:1-2.

How should youth respond to older men? ________________________________
Younger men? ____
Older women? ____
Younger women? _____________________________________

An older brother will protect his younger sister and that is how young men should act towards all young ladies. Boys, you are a warrior prince with God, the King, as your father. Walk like such – rescuing damsels in distress and talking and thinking respectfully about them. Girls, you are to treat the guys like brothers. They need to be encouraged and praised in Godly ways. A sister would not flaunt her body for a brother, and a brother will not think inappropriate thoughts towards a sister. This stage should last until the time that you are ready for marriage both emotionally and financially.

It is a good idea to go out and spend your leisure time with groups made up of boys and girls during this stage. For single children or a boy from an all boy family or a girl from an all girl family, this is a great time to stand back and figure out the other sex. Watch how they interact with others of their own sex and the opposite sex. God created boys and girls very differently. Good friendships at this level should be Godly and encouraging. Study the Bible together, seek to serve God together as a group.

You may decide at this stage that God has called you to be single for a longer period of time or permanently. Jesus honors this decision in Matthew 19:10.

Start in verse 9 and read through verse 12.

It is a gift to some that God gives to be able to go through life without a spouse and with God alone. I have a friend who has made this choice and a godlier woman I have never seen.

She truly depends upon God for every decision. What strength she has. I, however, could not have lived a single life because of my personality and need for intimacy both physical and emotional. Husbands can be good things to have around.

So, the next stage begins when you feel that God has prepared you financially, emotionally, and spiritually to be a husband or a wife. Notice I did not say to get a husband or a wife. You need to be sure that you are complete in Christ apart from a spouse before you seek to marry. Become a whole, healthy individual before you try to contribute to a marriage. This stage rarely if ever begins at 16, the acceptable age according to society to start dating. Become the best person that you can be, seek to grow in your career, your walk with God, and emotionally. When that time comes, pray about the person that God would have you to court and date.

Spend time with the other person in group settings, in family settings with both pairs of parents, and in public places as a couple. Begin to ask questions and discern if this other person's life is running in the direction that you feel God is calling you. Are their values the same as yours? Are their priorities the same? Do you agree on family issues such as how many children to have, when to have children, the place of the mother in the home, etc. This is a time of open and honest communication. There should be little to no physical touching at this point.

After a time of getting to know one another, both need to decide if you are ready to pursue a relationship towards marriage. Pray together, with your parents, and alone. Spend time planning and dreaming realistically. Talk together with a pastor or counselor or other respected adult to hash out communication differences and relational idiosyncrasies. For example, after a disagreement, one of you might need time alone to sort through your thoughts and the other one might expect you both to talk it out together immediately. Learning each other's habits and needs will help you get through the tough times a little easier. Notice that the physical relationship is not really in the picture. Save that for after the wedding.

So you are both sure that he/she is the one. You've prayed about it, and both sets of parents are giving their blessing. Set a wedding date and enjoy the last few days of single life. Spend time with other friends, with family, and of course, with each other. It is still best to agree to meet around others in a public place. Long engagements are frustrating. You are human and you do have those darn hormones running wild. I strongly suggest no more than a six-month engagement unless circumstances don't allow that.

So, the bells are ringing, the bride is blushing, and the groom is smiling from ear to ear. Those magic words are said and you are now husband and wife. Congratulations.

Now the work begins: learning to blend two different people into one. There are two backgrounds, two personalities, two families of origin, two approaches to everything. (And one is not right and the other wrong. Just different.).

Enjoy this time, but remember to talk and talk and talk. Don't walk out on a disagreement, push through it. My husband and I agreed early on to touch one another when we had a disagreement. Sometimes that was only a fingertip to a knee, but it kept us talking. Divorce was never an option for us. (In as much as your ability to control the situation – God does allow for divorce in cases of adultery).

So, figure it out. If you are both in careers and time is short, it is harder to find the time and energy to work through life. Keep things simple. Set aside a night each week for a date night. This is essential especially when children start arriving. Look at each other. Oh, and did I mention to talk, talk, talk.? Be honest with each other. Don't try to protect one another. No secrets are allowed from spouses. If you have to keep it a secret, don't do it.

Write out below the things that you would desire in a spouse – characteristics, habits, lifestyle, etc.

Realistic Relationships

Lesson 74

"As a bird that wandereth from her nest,
so is a man that wandereth from his place."
Proverbs 27:8

This is true for men and women. The home must be a priority. It is in a home that you grow as a Christian and as a person. It is a safe place. It is where love rules and children are nurtured. It is where you can get recharged, lick your wounds and recover, and are protected and secure. Not all homes are this way because of sin. If you did not grow up in a home where you were safe, you can still provide that for your spouse and children with God's love and healing.

Women, this is not a popular teaching in today's world, but it is Biblical. Titus 2:2-8 has a lot to teach us about the home and the relationships and priorities within that home.

Older men would include any who are spiritually mature and have taken on the responsibility of wife or wife and children.

List the characteristics given for an older man.
1.
2.
3.
4.
5.
6.

List the characteristics for an older woman.
1.
2.
3.
4.
5.

List the characteristics that the older woman is to teach the younger women.
1.
2.
3.
4.
5.
6.
7.

What reason is given in Titus 2:5 for such behavior? ____________________________

____

List the characteristics of a young man.
1.
2.
3.
4.
5.
6.

That's a lot to live up to. Okay, girls, here it is. You are to be workers at home. This does not mean that you can't have a job in or out of the house. What it does mean is that the home should be your top priority. When things are going smoothly at home, all members of the family are more secure, more relaxed, and are able to focus on other things. I have found that it is essential to stay at home with the children when they are young. They need the security and training of their parents. I have worked in childcare facilities and would never put my children in one. A home of a grandparent or other loving adult might be an option if the woman must work. But home is best. There the children will grow up with a sense of belonging, feeling loved, secure, safe, and ready to venture into new situations. The home is the foundation.

We chose to continue to homeschool our children through the high school years. This is an individual choice and is between each family and God.

Deuteronomy 6:7 tells us that it is our responsibility to teach God's precepts and Words to our children.

Read at Deuteronomy 6:7-9. When should you teach your children about God?

____

____

It requires time and relationship to teach and model a Godly life for our children. This is best accomplished at home. I see too many parents who brought their children to church since they were young and can't understand why they have chosen to go astray in their teenage years and early adulthood. And, yet, most of these children were raised in a secular school situation spending 8 hours a day hearing things contrary to God's Word. The home must be our first tower of defense. Careers can wait. Children cannot. They will grow up with or without the Word and with or without parents – this will shape their lives.

For Guys

(But good for the girls to go through as well)

Lesson 75

"Whoso findeth a wife findeth a good thing,
and obtaineth favour of the Lord"
Proverbs 18:22

Okay guys, it's your turn. We will be looking at yesterday's word from Titus, but just for a few minutes let's see what else the Word has to say about marriage. Turn to these verses and write down your thoughts on how a man should behave according to these verses.

Psalm 127:1 ____

____

Matthew 7:24 ____

____

Ephesians 5:25, 28 _______________________________________

____

Ephesians 5:33 ____

____

1 Peter 3:7 ____

____

Colossians 3:19 ____

____

There are many other verses including many that we have gone over in Proverbs about the love a man should have for his wife and the loyalty that he should honor.

In the book, His Needs, Her Needs, by Willard F. Harley, Jr. (a great book for young couples to read together. It is subtitled: Building an Affair-Proof Marriage) the author explains that a woman's first need is for affection. Affection includes words of affirmation, hugging, kissing, hand holding, non-sexual touching, and a wink of acknowledgement while in a crowd. Men's greatest need is sexual fulfillment. This is defined as: sex. Pure and simple.

There is a cycle here. If you meet her needs, she will be filled up to meet your needs. If she meets your needs, you will be full up to meet hers, etc. So if your needs are not being met, humble yourself and give that unconditional affection. The way to get your needs met is to meet her needs. This requires humility. Yes, you are to be the leader of the home, but a servant leader. Lead by example. Be strong, but gentle in your decisions. Listen to your wife; she often has insight (woman's intuition) that will help you make a better decision. Do life together. Oh yeah, and talk, talk, talk.

Back to Titus 2. Let's review the characteristics of a younger man.

1. To be sensible
2. An example of good deeds
3. Pure in doctrine
4. Dignified
5. Sound in speech
6. Beyond reproach

When you take on the responsibility of a family, it is time to grow up. It is no longer about you. It is time to be sensible – thinking through to the consequences of your actions and words; planning ahead for the financial stability of your family; putting the needs of others above your own. It is time to be an example of good deeds. Your wife and children will look to you as a godly example of leadership, servanthood, unconditional love, responsibility, and godly fun. Having come from an abusive home, my husband's unconditional love paved the way for me to truly accept God's fatherhood for myself. As he exhibited these traits and characteristics, I learned what it meant to be loved by a God who was my Heavenly Father.

Men, be pure in doctrine. Be the spiritual leaders of your home. Your wife should not be the one initiating prayer, taking the kids to church, teaching Bible stories, etc... That is your role. And to do it well, you need to have spent time on your own knees and in the Word so that your teaching is correct and accurate. Having other godly men in your life will also help with this.

Be dignified, sound in speech, and beyond reproach. Grow up. You are no longer a little boy. Be a man. That doesn't mean that you can't have fun, just save the fun for appropriate times and share the fun with your family. Just a note: It is not appropriate for man to have a friendship with another woman aside from his wife. Other couples are fun to get together with, but your relationship should be with the man, not the woman. (That goes as well for the woman. Woman friends are great. Leave their husbands to your husband.)

Make your speech sound. Watch your words. Little ears are listening. Live beyond reproach. Don't do in secret what you can't do in the light. This all sounds like a lot of do's and don'ts, but they will safeguard your marriage and bring you happier times than you can imagine.

Cherish is the word that I think of when I think about how a husband should treat his wife. She is precious, breakable, beautiful, and a princess. You should treasure her insight, her input, her personality, and her gifts. Together you can be so much more than either of you could be on your own if you cherish your wife.

There is a list of books in appendix D that will greatly help you prepare for marriage. Check them out.

For Girls

(Boys read this, too.)

Lesson 76

"As a jewel of gold in a swine's snout,
so is a fair woman which is without discretion."
Proverbs 11:22

I really didn't make that up. It really is in God's Word! But what does it mean? Let's compare it to a verse in Proverbs 31. Look at Proverbs 31:30.

What characteristic is desired more than beauty? ______________________________

That's right. All the money and time that we spend on being beautiful is for nothing if our hearts and attitudes are not right before the Lord. The Bible does not forbid the wearing of jewelry and make-up etc., but it does caution us not to be merely about our looks. Let's look up a couple more verses.

1 Timothy 2:9-10 What should come before beauty? __________________________
____

1 Peter 3:4 What is precious in God's sight? ______________________________
____

There is nothing wrong with being attractive, wearing nice clothes, or using hair products. But those things will not draw us closer to God or, eventually, to our husbands. Be a woman of substance. Be someone that is valuable for their sweet and tender spirit before God. It is a true statement that in a home, the mother sets the tone. Is your home going to be beautiful, but your children afraid to touch anything? Is cheerfulness and joy going to abound, or will everyone get up each morning hoping that Mom is not in another bad mood? You are going to be the feminine example for your children. Girls will emulate you and your boys will look to you to see what they should be looking for in a wife someday. Be a woman of the Word, gentle and caring.

I really struggled with the "gentle and quiet spirit" of 1 Peter. God gave me a voice that does not need a microphone in a gymnasium or on a ball field. My personality is that of a cheerleader. I love laughter and good conversation. Growing up a Yankee gave me the ability to talk fast and get excited. If I interrupt someone it is just enthusiasm and not rudeness.

I moved to the South at age 19; what a culture shock! My mind was several paragraphs ahead as I listened to the slow southern drawl of most my peers. But God showed me that even I can have a gentle and quiet spirit. God made some of us French horns. The thought goes in, rambles around for a while and comes out mellow and complete. Others of us are like trumpets. It's out our mouths before we have time to think and it is usually loud and center stage.

Which are you, a French horn or a trumpet? ________________

Whichever you are, as long as you are playing God's song for your life and listening as He conducts, your music will be beautiful.

God made hand tools and power tools. If you are a hand tool, then let God's hand guide your path. But if you are a power tool, then be sure that you are plugged in to God's power source. Either tool can have a gentle and quiet heart. Some of us just like to tell others about it a little more and a little louder.

Let's look for a few minutes at the verses in Titus that describe a young woman.

List the eight characteristics that an older woman is to teach a younger woman in Titus 2:3-5.

1.
2.
3.
4.
5.
6.
7.
8.

Number one is to learn to love your husband. This is not infatuation, first year honeymoon love, but deep, unconditional abiding love that will carry you through life's bumps and bruises. Dr. James Dobson says that the most important relationship for any child is not the child's relationship to their mom or to their dad, but rather the relationship between their mom and dad. Why is this? It is from their parents' example that they receive security, safety, a sense of worth and love. "If Mom and Dad don't love each other, then how can they love me (their child)?" Remember, kids see and interpret things from a kid's viewpoint. So the marriage relationship needs to be your top priority. Your husband should come before your career. Your children should come before your career, and, of course, your walk with God should be above all else.

Loving your children extends beyond caring for their physical needs. That is a part of it, but they are young and impressionable. What impression do you want to make upon them? This will take time and attention. This will take habit of being there and memories of mom's consistency. You can do it. There is no greater joy than motherhood when the children have been raised to mind, to love, and to work. Then surely Proverbs 10:1 can become a reality.

Titus 2 says that you are to be sensible. That means to run the home with forethought and wisdom. Budgeting, nutrition, cleanliness, routine, etc. fall under this topic. Be a student of other great women that have gone before you. Learn from their books, their lives, their examples and pattern your home after Godly women. Your home should exude peace and tranquility (even with toddlers about.) See the book suggestions in Appendix D.

The next characteristic is to be pure. This is not only in sexual areas, but also in your thought life. Be aware that what you put into your mind will mold your character. Soap operas, romance novels, etc. are not appropriate entertainment material for a Christian woman. There are a lot of movies and books that are encouraging and uplifting. Focus on these. Purity in speech includes not gossiping, not cursing, not speaking in anger, etc. A general rule is that if you don't want it overheard, don't say it.

We already spoke about being workers at home. The next trait is to be kind. Go about doing good. Speak words of kindness. Look for ways to serve others. The best way to make a friend is to be a friend. Don't forget your girlfriends once you marry. You need each other. God created women for relationships. Keep a balance between friends and husband.

Being subject to your own husband is not being a door mat. It means that you dress modestly, look to your husband for leadership, protection, and provision. It means respecting him and building him up. It means meeting his needs. When his needs are met, then he is ready to meet yours as well. It means being the wonderful princess that God created you to be, but understanding that God also ordained for you to be cared for by another.

Respect is huge for our men. Ephesians 5:33 says that the man should love his wife, but that the wife should respect her husband. And he needs to hear that respect through your words of affirmation. Take time to say "good job," or "Wow, I could never have done that, you are so talented." Tell him how much you appreciate it when he helps you in the kitchen; that may make him want to volunteer again.

Gracious Girls

(Boys do this lesson also.)

Lesson 77

"A virtuous woman is a crown to her husband:
but she that maketh ashamed is as rottenness in his bones."
Proverbs 12:4

Proverbs has a lot more to say for the women. Let's look at a few more verses. Tell how these verses can be used in a practical way.

Proverbs 14:1 ____
____

Proverbs 14:4. This one will take some thought. Think about how people are more important than things. ____________________________________
____

Proverbs 18:22 ____
____

Proverbs 19:13 ____
____

Proverbs 19:14 ____
____

Proverbs 21:9 ____
____

Proverbs 21:19 ____
____

Proverbs 27:15-16 ____
____

Did you notice a recurring theme? So what is a contentious woman? It is a woman who is looking for a fight, a woman who is always right, a woman who never speaks words of respect to her husband, and a woman who is not filled with the Spirit of God. To keep from being contentious, be in the Word, constantly praying and praising God for His goodness, encouraging your husband, and bringing joy and unity to the home.

Wise Woman

Lesson 78

"Favour is deceitful, and beauty is vain:
but a woman that feareth the Lord,
she shall be praised."
Proverbs 31:30

Guys this verse is a good measuring stick for the woman of your dreams, and girls this is a good standard to set to make a happy husband. However, it is also perfection and impossible without God. The best commentary I ever heard on Proverbs 31 was that the writer was from the perspective of a woman who was older and looking back on her life. In the different seasons of life, she was able to accomplish all of the tasks – not all at once. Talk about one tired girl. Let's look at these wonderful verses, actually a poem written by the wisest man that ever lived.

Look at verse 10.

What is an excellent wife compared to? ________________

Notice that she is not as good as fine jewels, but her worth is far above jewels.

Verse 11 talks about trust. It is so important in the marriage relationship for both parties to be able to trust the other. This means open and honest conversation. This means no tale telling to girlfriends or co-workers. Honor your spouse in your words to others. Don't get into the trap of one upping your companions. Commit to keep secret and between the two of you your sex life and your emotional intimacy. Protect one another. Proverbs 31 says that this will bring great gain.

The excellent wife has what kind of actions for her husband?

____

These actions are not reactionary, but take the initiative – the initiative to serve him with meals, and a clean house, and clean clothes; the initiative to massage his tired muscles or kidnap him from work for a picnic. (Marriage can be a lot of fun.)

Verses 13 and 14 seem odd in our culture. Today it would read: "She shops for clothes that will enhance his looks, and delights in washing and ironing them with her hands.
She gathers food from the market and feeds her family well." (The author's version)

Verse 15 tells of her untiring love and the priority that she places on her home.

Verse 16 suggests that she is a shrewd business woman. She is careful with the household finances and uses them wisely.

What can you do to earn extra income while making your home your priority?

____

For me, it was teaching piano lessons from my home. It might be baking or sewing for others, doing work on the computer, watching other's children, or doing a professional job from home.

Verse 17 tells us that she takes care of herself. She exercises regularly and stays fit. But I think it also speaks of strength of character that comes from growing in her walk with Jesus.

Verse 18 speaks of the contentment and self-fulfillment that a woman gains by doing her job well. That motivates her to work into the night at times. (Last minute science projects or a husband who comes home late discouraged.) She does this with a quiet and gentle spirit, ready to serve, and eager to help.

Verse 19 again tells of her prowess with household responsibilities. We no longer have to make our own thread to weave our own clothes, but we should be learning and growing in areas of meal planning and preparation, laundry, even gardening and canning, knitting or sewing. I admit that when God handed out the computer chips, I was not in the line for cooking. I have a magnet on my refrigerator that claims that the only reason I have a kitchen is that it came with the house. I would much rather be writing or teaching. But I have muddled through, read cookbooks, tried a few new things, and managed to feed a family of 7 for years. Now, baking bread and brownies? I am your woman for that. Unfortunately, man cannot live on bread and brownies alone. Try something new, you might find you like it.

Verse 20 shows the generosity of an excellent wife. She is able from her abundance, because of her careful management of the house, to share with those less fortunate. It's really fun to see someone in need of food and buy them groceries, leave them on their front porch, and run. They only know that God supplied (you were His servant.) It is fun to make up Christmas baskets for another family that lost their job. Helping others is being a great example to your kids. They can get into the spirit of things by reading to an older adult or playing a board game with a neighbor that can't get out much. Use your imagination and pray for opportunities to help others.

Verses 21-24 speaks of her ability to not only clothe her family, but to do it well. They are wearing garments of purple and scarlet which were only worn by royalty. But remember, you are a daughter of the King, your husband is a prince, and your children little princes and princesses. Even if you can't afford expensive clothing, they can be neat and well cared for. Teach your children to clothe themselves in honor and humility, contentment and joy – no matter what their outer garments may be.

In verse 25, what does the excellent wife wear? ______________________________

____

And because of this she is not afraid of the future. Where does the strength and dignity come from? Her relationship with God and her husband.

In verse 26 what two things also come from this same source?

____

Woman's Work and Worth

Lesson 79

"She looks well to the ways of her household,
And does not eat the bread of idleness."
Proverbs 31:27

Let's finish up this great passage on a woman's work and worth.

Verse 27 tells us that she looks well to the ways of her household and is not lazy. Her time is not filled up with idle chatter, and shallow friendships. Her priority is her home.

Verses 28-29 always remind of the time one of my children threw some words back into my face. When they would fuss over doing chores, I would tell them that someday they would bow down and call me blessed. One day, as I stepped out of the bathroom, my eight-year old ran through the hallway, threw himself down at my feet, clasped his hands in front of him and yelled "Blessed". He then jumped up and ran outside. I called him back in to find out what he was doing. He said, "You're always saying that one day I will bow down and call you blessed, well I thought I would do it now and get it out of the way." He is now 19 and has a much better understanding of what that phrase means and he often thanks me for the lessons he learned and the discipline that he received. He is a fine young man.

Have you called your mother blessed? Maybe not in those words, but have you thanked her for all that she does? How can you tell your mother how much you appreciate her?

____

Praise from her husband is her reward. What greater joy can a woman have than for her husband to brag about her to others? He holds her in high esteem. He recognizes her worth. She will walk on clouds for days after her beloved repeats such praises to his friends or family. And she has earned it. It is not flattery; it is truth. She has spent time with her God, used her gifts wisely, loved her husband and children well, been kind to others, and she is at peace with herself, content and joyful. Verse 31 says that the works of her hands speak for themselves of her greatness. When people say that we have done a great job raising our five boys, my response is that the proof is in the pudding and the pudding is not done yet. Well, the pudding is almost finished and I am proud of five young men that love God, desire to raise Godly children, and are a joy and a blessing to their Mom and Dad.

I am now going to take a side issue and discuss abuse in the marriage for one minute. You are human. Your spouse is human. You will make mistakes. You sin and need forgiveness. If one spouse is not a Christian, then it is very hard to reach a balance in a marriage. God warns us not to be unequally yoked with unbelievers. (2 Corinthians 6:14). Even when both partners are believers, one can be acting out of foolishness and unbelief. If there is physical or emotional abuse in the marriage, it is wise to separate until the time that there is

repentance and healing. Notice that I did not say divorce.

It is never okay to stay in an abusive relationship. Princes and princesses are too precious to be used that way. But God does lay down some guidelines for divorce. (Divorce is permissible if the other partner has been sexually unfaithful. However, I have seen couples restored with greater intimacy after an affair through much prayer and Godly counsel. But both parties will need to desire this restoration. You can't do it alone.) If you are truly living a Godly life and your spouse is abusive, get help. Abuse is when the other person is allowed to have their own ideas, thoughts, opinions, or feelings. Seek God's direction. Bottom line, don't be abusive, and get help if your spouse is being abusive. No one deserves abuse.

What actions or words do you think constitute abuse? ______________________

____

Decide now that you will never engage in such behavior or allow another to abuse you.

What is love? Love is not an emotion or conditional. Love is a covenantal promise. So, when you say, "I love you," it is a promise to stay by and respect and serve the other for life. This is the way that God loves you. Love is not based on your performance, or how someone meets your expectations; it is a forever commitment based on the relationship. You are God's child. Period. Nothing you can do will change that relationship.

You might get out of fellowship with God because of sin, but you will still be His. In a marriage, this is also true. I may not always like what my husband does; I may not even always like him, but he will always be my husband and I will remain committed to that relationship until death. When you can understand this, then you realize how important it is to communicate and work through every disagreement, fight, or frustration with your spouse. And, you begin to really understand the love of God for you.

Write out Romans 8:38-39. ____

____

____

____

How great is God's love for you? ____________________________________

You can learn to love your spouse with that same kind of love.

God is…

Lesson 80

"The Lord is my shepherd."
Psalm 23:1

How would you fill out the rest of this statement?

God is…

____

____

The God of the Bible is so many things to his children. That is why He has so many names. As God revealed Himself to his children in the Old Testament, He revealed another one of His names. As they walked through their lives, God revealed more and more to them about His character. Here are some of His names:

Jehovah – (Lord God) "He who is truly present"; eternal; Self-existent.

Adonai – (Lord, plural) The One high and above all things; the Owner of all there is; Lord and Master

Elohim – El-unlimited strength, energy, might, and power
Alah-to swear, declare or make a covenant.
Therefore, Elohim – to the covenanted ones, I AM a supply of strength, energy, might, and power. He is totally dependable.

El-Shaddai – (God Almighty) Giver and Sustainer of life.

El-Elyon – (Most High God) The Possessor of heaven and earth; Omnipotent; the Strongest Strong One.

El-Olam – (The everlasting God) eternal duration, everlasting, evermore. God's timelessness, His vast knowledge and His constancy and stability.

El-Roi – (The God Who Sees) One who watches over us, concerning Himself with our needs.

Jehovah-Jireh – (The Lord Will Provide) Ultimately through Jesus Christ.

Jehovah-Nissi – (The Lord is My Banner) All power is with Him; all strength comes from Him; our victory.

Jehovah-Tsidkenu –	(The Lord Our Righteousness) The only truly righteous One; the absolute, impeccable standard.
Jehovah-Roah –	(The Lord is My Shepherd) One tending, pasturing, leading, feeding, and protecting very dependent creatures.

We also learn to relate to different aspects of God as we grow as a Christian. I first accepted God as God the Creator, then God of history and the Bible. Later I accepted Him as my Savior. Soon He began being my Lord in all areas of my life. It took a while, but eventually He became my shepherd as I trusted Him with my provision and protection. He became my King; I would do anything for Him out of obedience. Soon after this, He became my Friend. I could walk with Him and talk with Him and tell Him anything. I knew He was always there. Lastly, for me, He became my Heavenly Father. I could sit in His lap and fully trust Him. I am not to the point of understanding God fully as my Bridegroom, but as I fellowship with Him daily, I pray that that time will come. It is a journey. It was painful at times as God revealed my pride, or sinfulness, or unbelief to me. But always He was there to heal the wounds and claim Himself Sufficient in all things.

How has God revealed Himself to you? Not in your intellect but experientially? Where has your journey taken you and where do you need to head? Meditate on the names of God and rejoice over your victories.

Circle the names of God that are a reality in your life (not just knowledge) and then move forward by praying and asking God to show Himself to you as these other names as well.

Faithful	Forgiving	Salvation	Master and Lord
Source of Strength	Shelter	Creator	Architect and Builder
Defender	King of Kings	Father	God Almighty
My Rock	God of Grace	God of Hope	God of Love
God of Peace	The Truth	The Life	Holy Father
The Great Physician	God Who is There	Provider	Protector
Comforter	Shepherd	Friend	All Sufficient One
The Potter	Alpha and Omega	Bridegroom	Refuge
Judge	Anchor		

I hope you have enjoyed this journey through Proverbs. I will leave you with James 1:5.

> "If any of you lack wisdom, let him ask of God, that giveth to all men liberally, and upbraideth not; and it shall be given him."

Appendix A

FOOLISHNESS: CHARACTERISTICS AND RESULTS

	Characteristics	**Results**
1:7	despises wisdom and instruction	takes away life of its possessor

Characteristics	Results

Characteristics	Results

Characteristics	Results

Appendix B

WISDOM: CHARACTERISTICS AND RESULTS

	Characteristics	**Results**
1:23		

Characteristics | **Results**

Characteristics	Results

Characteristics	Results

Appendix C

Proverbs 3:1-26 (KJV)

1 My son, forget not my law;

but let thine heart keep my commandments:

2 For length of days, and years of life,

and peace, shall they add to thee.

3 Let not mercy and truth forsake thee:

bind them about thy neck:

write them upon the table of thine heart:

4 So shalt thou find favour and good understanding

in the sight of God and man.

5 Trust in the Lord with all thine heart;

and lean not unto thine own understanding.

6 In all thy ways acknowledge him,

and he shall direct thy paths.

7 Be not wise in thine own eyes:

fear the Lord, and depart form evil.

8 It shall be health to thy navel,

and marrow to thy bones.

9 Honour the Lord with thy substance,

and with the firstfruits of all thine increase:

10 So shall thy barns be filled with plenty,

and thy presses shall burst out with new wine.

11 My son, despise not the chastening of the Lord;

neither be weary of his correction:

12 For whom the Lord loveth he correcteth;

even as a father the son in whom he delighteth.

13 Happy is the man that findeth wisdim,

and the man that getteth understanding.

14 For the merchandise of it is better than the merchandise of silver,

and the gain thereof than fine gold.

15 She is more precious than rubies:

and all the things thou canst desire are not to be compared unto her.

16 Length of days is in her right hand;

and in her left hand riches and honour.

17 Her ways are ways of pleasantness,

and all her paths are peace.

18 She is a tree of life to them that lay hold upon her:

and happy is every one that retaineth her.

19 The Lord by wisdom hath founded the earth;

by understanding hath he established the heavens.

20 By his knowledge the depths are broken up,

and the clouds drop down the dew.

21 My son, let not them depart from thine eyes:

keep sound wisdom and discretion:

22 So shall they be life unto thy soul,

and grace to thy neck.

23 Then shalt thou walk in thy way safely,

and thy foot shall not stumble.

24 When thou liest down, thou shalt not be afraid:

yea, thou shalt lie down, and thy sleep shall be sweet.

25 Be not afraid of sudden fear,

neither of the desolation of the wicked, when it cometh.

26 For the Lord shall be thy confidence,

and shall keep thy foot from being taken.

Appendix D

Recommended Reading:

Burkett, Larry, *Money Management Workbook for College Students,* (Moody Publishers, 1998)

Carter, Les, *The Anger Workbook,* (Thomas Nelson, 1992).

Carter, Les, *The Choosing to Forgive Workbook*, (Thomas Nelson, 1997).

Chapman, Gary, *The Five Love Languages,* (Northwood Press, 2010).

Colson, Chuck, *How Now Shall We Live?* (Tyndale House Publishers, 2004).

DeMoss, Nancy L., Surrender: *The Heart God Controls* (Chicago, IL.: Moody Publ., 2003).

Dillow, Linda, *Creative Counterpart*, (Thomas Nelson, 1977).

Dobson, James, *Life on the Edge: The Next Generation's Guide to a Meaningful Future,* (Tyndale House, 2007).

Eggerichs, Dr. Emerson, *Love & Respect: The Love She Most Desires, The Respect He Desperately Needs,* (Thomas Nelson, 2004).

Elliott, Elizabeth, *Passion and Purity,* (Revell, 2002).

Erickson-Tada, Joni, *When God Weeps: Why Our Suffering Matters to the Almighty,* (Zondervan, 1997).

Freed, Jeffrey, *Right Brained Kids in a Left Brained World*, (Simon & Schuster, 1988).

Gillham, Bill, *Lifetime Guarantee*, (Harvest House Publishers, 1993).

Gillham, Anabel, *The Confident Woman: Knowing Who You Are in Christ,* (Eugene, Oregon: Harvest House, 1993).

Gresh, Dannah, *And the Bride Wore White,* (Moody Publishers, 2004).

Harley, William F, *His Needs, Her Needs,* (Revell, 2001).

Harris, Joshua, *I Kissed Dating Goodbye*, (Doubleday Religious publishing Group, 2003).

Harris, Joshua, *Boy Meets Girl*, (Multnomah Books, 2000).

Kilgo, Edith Flowers, *Handbook for Christian Homemakers,* (Baker Book House, 1982).

Lewis, C.S., *Mere Christianity*, (Macmillan Publishers, 1952). Other publishers also available.

Ludy, Eric, *When God Writes Your Love Story*, (Multnomah, 2004).

Mathis, Dale and Susan, *Countdown for Couples: Preparing for the Adventure of Marriage,* (Focus on the Family, 2008).

Moore, Beth, *Believing God*, (B&H Publishing Group, 2004).

Ortlund, Anne, *Children are Wet Cement,* (Power Books, Fleming H. Revell Co., 1978).

Ortlund, Anne, *Disciplines of a Beautiful Woman*, (Word Books, 1984).

Parrott, Les and Leslie, *Saving Your Marriage Before It Starts*, (Zondervan, 2006).

Paulsen, Heather Arnel, *Emotional Purity,* (Crossway Books, 2007).

Schaeffer, Francis, *The Christian Manifesto*, (Crossway Books, 1982).

Schaeffer, Francis, *The God Who Is There*, (Crossway Publishers, 1990).

Schaeffer, Francis, *The Mark of a Christian,* (IVP Classics, 2006).

Silvious, Jan, *Foolproofing Your Life*, (Doubleday Religious Publishing Group, 1998).

Sire, James W., *The Universe Next Door*, (IVP Academic, 1994).

Terkekurst, Lysa, *Capture Her Heart: Becoming the Godly Husband Your Wife Desires,* (Moody Publishers, 2002).

Thomas, Gary L., *Sacred Marriage: What if God Designed Marriage to Make Us Holy More Than to Make Us Happy,* (Zondervan, 2002.)

Thurman, Dr. Chris, *The Lies We Believe*, (Thomas Nelson Publishers, 1989).

Notes: Lesson 29

Dear Reader, I checked in several commentaries and each one agreed. Here is what I found:

The Nestle-Aland and Westcott and Hort Greek texts do not consider this phrase as legitimate. It is probable that a copyist inadvertently picked up the phrase from Romans 8:4 which has the identical wording.
Can you see how this additional phrase leads to a slightly different interpretation of "no condemnation"? Paul is not basing his declaration of no condemnation upon our conduct, but upon our position (in Christ). While it is true that those who are in Christ should not and do not consistently walk according to the flesh, this is not a condition for their status of "no condemnation" and for that we are thank our merciful Father for the wisdom and perfection of His plan of salvation.
The Net Bible also adds this note: "The earliest and best witnesses of the Alexandrian and Western texts have no additional words for v1. Both the external evidence and the internal evidence are completely compelling for the shortest reading. The scribes were obviously motivated to add such qualifications (interpolated from v4), for otherwise Paul's gospel smelled too much of grace.".
Dr Harry Ironside has an interesting thought on the variation in translations remarking that:,

> Careful students of the original text discover that the last part of Romans 8:1 in the King James version is an interpolation properly belonging to verse 4 [Romans 8:4]. The magnificent statement that opens Romans 8, "There is therefore now no condemnation to them which are in Christ Jesus" – requires no qualifying clause. Our justification does not depend on our walk. Freedom from condemnation is given to all who are in Christ, and to be in Him means to be of the new creation. A glance at the Revised version or any critical translation will show that what I am pointing out is sustained by all the editors. It was man's innate aversion to sovereign grace, I am certain, that brought these qualifying words into the text of the King James version. It seemed too much to believe that freedom from condemnation depended solely on being in Christ Jesus and not on our walking after the Spirit. So it was easy to lift the words from verse 4 [Romans 8:4-note] into verse 1 [Romans 8:1]. But in verse 4 [Romans 8:4] they have their proper place for there Paul was writing of the state of the believer. In verse 1 [Romans 8:1] it is the question of standing that is under consideration. (Romans and Galatians Ironside, Harry: Expository Commentaries)

You can read more at: http://preceptaustin.org/new_page_61.htm